JUNIOR CERTI

Maths Revision
Higher Level
Paper 2

Brendan Guildea & Louise Boylan

g GILL EDUCATION

Gill Education
Hume Avenue
Park West
Dublin 12
www.gilleducation.ie

Gill Education is an imprint of M.H. Gill & Co.

Print origination and artwork by MPS Limited

The paper used in this book is made from the wood pulp of managed forests.
For every tree felled, at least one tree is planted, thereby renewing natural resources.

For permission to reproduce photographs, the authors and publisher gratefully
acknowledge the following:

© Shutterstock: 110, 159, 160, 161, 162; © Shutterstock/Daniel Hixon: 129;
© Shutterstock/Luis Santos: 122; © Shutterstock/Michael Winston Rosa: 7.

The author and publisher have made every effort to trace all copyright holders, but if
any has been inadvertently overlooked we would be pleased to make the necessary
arrangement at the first opportunity.

Acknowledgements

The authors would like to thank Carol Guildea, Joe Heron and Paula Keogh.

CONTENTS

Please note:

- The philosophy of Project Maths is that topics can overlap, so you may encounter Paper 1 material on Paper 2 and vice versa.
- The Exam questions marked by the symbol ⬡ in this book are selected from the following:
  1. SEC Exam papers
  2. Sample exam papers
  3. Original and sourced exam-type questions

Introduction

The aim of this revision book is to help you get as high a mark as possible in your Junior Certificate Higher Level maths exam. This book is designed to be exam focused. To do this, the book is based not just on the syllabus, but also on the examination paper. Because of this, this revision book can be used in conjunction with **any** textbook.

Graded examples and exam questions

Throughout this book, **examples and exam questions are graded by level of difficulty**.

The level of difficulty is indicated by calculator symbols, as follows:

The number of calculators shown beside a question helps you know how difficult the question is. One calculator indicates a question which is relatively basic. As the questions get harder, there will be more calculators. Three calculators indicate an average level question, whereas five calculators indicate that it is a very challenging question. These questions may be beyond some students, but give them a go! Students hoping to achieve an A grade should aim to complete all of the five-calculator questions. The calculator symbol given for each question relates to the most difficult part of that question. Don't be discouraged by a challenging question. As in the Junior Certificate exam, difficult questions can sometimes begin with one or two simple parts. You should attempt as much as you can.

Preparing for your Junior Certificate Maths exam

It is very important to realise that **you are your own best teacher**. Revision is when you begin to teach yourself. Thus, it is very important for you to start your revision as soon as possible. Make notes while you are revising. If you are having difficulty with a particular question, seek help from your teacher, a friend or a member of your family. As with all subjects, the best examination preparation is to work through past examination or sample papers so that you are familiar with the layout and the style of questions.

Let's start at the beginning. If you want to do well in your Junior Certificate, then two things are essential:

- Revise effectively.
- Be familiar with the exam paper and so be prepared on the day of the exam.

These may seem obvious, but it's worth taking a moment to think what these tips mean.

How to revise most effectively

If you are going to do well in the Junior Certificate, you need to spend quite a bit of time revising. Spending a little time learning how to revise effectively will help you to get more from your time and help you to absorb and understand more of the material on the course. Here are some tips to help you revise for maths.

- Find a quiet place where you can work. This place should be dedicated to study and free of potential distractions. Turn off the TV, computer and mobile phone.
- Write a study plan. Don't be afraid to ask your parents/teachers/guidance counsellor for help at this stage.
- Do the more challenging revision first, when you are fresh. Trying to focus on difficult problems when you are tired can be counter-productive.

Study in small chunks of time lasting 25 to 35 minutes. Your memory and concentration will work better if you study in short, frequent bursts.

- Project Maths is based on understanding, so while you can 'learn' some elements of the course, it is important that you develop an understanding of the material.
- Drill and practice are essential ingredients for success in maths.
- Try to link any new material to things you know already. This is learning through association and helps long-term retention.

Don't get hung up on more difficult material. Concentrate on understanding the fundamental concepts and being able to answer all of the straightforward questions. Then, with time, you can build up to the more challenging problems.

The Junior Certificate examination

Exam focus is critical to exam success. It is important to prepare yourself for the challenge you will face. By learning about the structure of the exam, you will learn how to maximise your points, allocate your time effectively and learn to manage the paper in a calm manner.

There is no set number of questions on this examination paper. You must answer **all** questions.

Questions do not necessarily carry equal marks. To help you manage your time during this examination, a maximum time for each question is suggested on the exam paper. **Do not spend more than the suggested time, on any question.**

Read the exam paper right through at the start, to determine which question is the easiest one to start with. Your mind may also be subconsciously processing some of the other problems.

If you remain within these times, you should have about 10 minutes left to review your work at the end of the exam.

Start with your best question. Then your next best and so on. This way, if you are short of time, at least your best questions will be done.

Attempt marks (partial credit) are valuable, so it is vital that you attempt all questions. Leave **NO** blanks.

Further exam tips

- There is no such thing as rough work in maths – all work is relevant. If the examiner doesn't know how you reached an answer – even a correct answer – then full marks will usually not be awarded. Thus, **show all your work**.
- It is a good idea to show each stage of a calculation when using a calculator (in case you press a wrong key). Familiarise yourself with your calculator. Know your book of tables and formulae well and write down any formula that you use.

Your calculator and book of tables are two extremely valuable resources to have in the exam. Make sure that you are very familiar with how your calculator works and that you know how to perform all functions on it. Also familiarise yourself with the book of tables so that there is no time wasted in the exam, trying to find formulae.

- Attempt marks will be awarded for any step in the right direction. Therefore, **make an attempt at each part of the question**. Even if you do not get the correct answer, you can still pick up most of the marks on offer if you show how you worked it out. Also, **draw a diagram where possible**, because this can help you to see the solution.

- If you cannot finish part of a question, leave a space and come back to it later. **Never scribble out any work or use Tipp-Ex**. Put a single line through it so that the examiner can still read it. **Avoid using pencil** because the writing can be very faint and difficult to read.

- If you run out of space in your answer booklet, **ask the supervisor for more paper**. Then clearly write the number of the exam question and the solution on the extra paper.

Glossary of words used on the examination paper

Write down, state
You can write down your answer without showing any work. However, if you want you can show some workings.

Calculate, Find, Show that, Determine, Prove
Obtain your answers by showing all relevant work. Marks are available for showing the steps leading to your final answer or conclusion.

Solve
Find the solution, or root, of an equation. The solution is the value of the variable that makes the left-hand side balance with the right-hand side.

Evaluate
Work out, or find, a numerical value by putting in numbers for letters.

Comment on
After studying the given information or your answers, give your opinion on their significance.

Plot
Indicate the position of points on a graph, usually on the x- and y-planes.

Construct
Draw an accurate diagram, usually labelled, using a pencil, ruler, set square, compass and protractor. Leave all construction lines on your diagram.

Sketch

Draw a rough diagram or graph, labelled if needed.

Hence

You must use the answer, or result, from the previous part of the question.

Hence or otherwise

It is recommended that you use the answer, or result, from the previous part of the question, and it is usually best to do this, but other methods are acceptable.

Syllabus checklist for Junior Certificate Higher Level Maths Paper 2 exam

The philosophy of Project Maths is that topics can overlap, so you may encounter Paper 1 material on Paper 2 and vice versa.

Throughout your course you will be asked to apply your knowledge and skills to solve problems in familiar and unfamiliar contexts. In problem solving, you should use some of the following strategies:

- Trial and improvement
- Draw a diagram
- Look for a pattern
- Act it out
- Draw a table

- Simplify the problem
- Use an equation
- Work backwards
- Eliminate possibilities

The syllabus stresses that in all aspects of the Junior Certificate Maths course, students should be able to:

- ☐ Explore patterns and formulate conjectures
- ☐ Explain findings
- ☐ Justify conclusions
- ☐ Communicate mathematics verbally and in written form
- ☐ Apply their knowledge and skills to solve problems in familiar and unfamiliar contexts
- ☐ Analyse information presented verbally and translate it into mathematical form
- ☐ Devise, select and use appropriate mathematical models, formulae or techniques to process information and to draw relevant conclusions

Coordinate Geometry

- [ ] Coordinating the plane
- [ ] Properties of lines and line segments, including:
  - Midpoint
  - Slope
  - Distance (length of a line segment)
  - Equation of a line in the form: $y - y_1 = m(x - x_1)$, $y = mx + c$ and $ax + by + c = 0$, where a, b, c, are integers and m is the slope of the line.
- [ ] Intersection of lines
- [ ] Explore the properties of points, lines and line segments, including the equation of a line.
- [ ] Find the point of intersection of two lines.
- [ ] Understand the relationships between the slopes of parallel and perpendicular lines.
- [ ] Find the slopes of parallel and perpendicular lines.

Synthetic Geometry

- [ ] Recall the axioms and use them in the solution of problems.
- [ ] Use the following terms: theorem, proof, axiom, corollary, converse and implies.
- [ ] Apply the results of all theorems, converses and corollaries to solve problems.
- [ ] Prove the specified Theorems (see Chapter 2 on theorems).
- [ ] Complete the constructions specified (see Chapter 3 on constructions).

Transformation Geometry

- [ ] Translations, central symmetry and axial symmetry.
- [ ] Locate axes of symmetry in simple shapes.
- [ ] Recognise images of points and objects under:
  - translation
  - central symmetry
  - axial symmetry.

Trigonometry

- [ ] Right-angled triangles
- [ ] Trigonometric ratios
- [ ] Work with trigonometric ratios in surd form for angles of 30°, 45° and 60°.
- [ ] Apply the theorem of Pythagoras to solve right-angled triangle problems of a simple nature involving heights and distances.
- [ ] Use trigonometric ratios to solve problems involving angles (integer values) between 0° and 90°.

☐ Solve problems involving surds.

☐ Solve problems involving right-angled triangles.

☐ Manipulate measure of angles in both decimal and DMS forms.

Applied Measure – Measure and Time

☐ 2D shapes and 3D solids, including nets of solids (two-dimensional representations of three-dimensional objects)

☐ Use nets to analyse figures and to distinguish between surface area and volume.

☐ Solve problems involving perimeter, surface area and volume.

☐ Model real-world situations and solve a variety of problems (including multi-step problems) involving surface areas, and volumes of cylinders and prisms.

☐ Learn about the circle and develop an understanding of the relationship between its circumference, diameter and π.

☐ Calculate, interpret and apply units of measure and time.

☐ Solve problems that involve calculating average speed, distance and time.

☐ Investigate the nets of rectangular solids.

☐ Find the volume of rectangular solids and cylinders.

☐ Find the surface area of rectangular solids.

☐ Identify the necessary information to solve a problem.

☐ Select and use suitable strategies to find length of the perimeter and the area of the following plane figures: disc, triangle, rectangle, square, and figures made from combinations of these.

☐ Draw and interpret scaled diagrams.

☐ Investigate nets of prisms (polygonal bases) cylinders and cones.

☐ Solve problems involving surface area of triangular-base prisms (right angle, isosceles, equilateral), cylinders and cones.

☐ Solve problems involving curved surface area of cylinders, cones and spheres.

☐ Perform calculations to solve problems involving the volume of rectangular solids, cylinders, cones, triangular base prisms (right angle, isosceles, equilateral), spheres and combinations of these.

Probability
Counting

☐ List outcomes of experiments in a systematic way.

☐ List all possible outcomes of an experiment.

☐ Apply the fundamental principle of counting.

Concepts of probability

- ☐ Calculate the probability of an event occurring: students progress from informal to formal descriptions of probability.
- ☐ Predict and determine probabilities.
- ☐ Understand the difference between experimental and theoretical probability.
- ☐ Decide whether an everyday event is likely or unlikely to occur.
- ☐ Recognise that probability is a measure on a scale of 0–1 of how likely an event is to occur.
- ☐ Use set theory to discuss experiments, outcomes and sample spaces.
- ☐ Use the language of probability to discuss events, including those with equally likely outcomes.
- ☐ Estimate probabilities from experimental data.
- ☐ Recognise that, if an experiment is repeated, there will be different outcomes and that increasing the number of times an experiment is repeated generally leads to better estimates of probability.
- ☐ Associate the probability of an event with its long-run, relative frequency.

Outcomes of simple random processes

- ☐ Find the probability of equally likely outcomes.
- ☐ Construct sample spaces for two independent events.
- ☐ Apply the principle that, in the case of equally likely outcomes, the probability is given by the number of outcomes of interest divided by the total number of outcomes (examples using coins, dice, spinners, turns with different coloured objects, playing cards, etc.).
- ☐ Use binary / counting methods to solve problems involving successive random events where only two possible outcomes apply to each event.

Statistics
Statistical reasoning with an aim to becoming a statistically aware consumer

- ☐ The use of statistics to gather information from a selection of the population with the intention of making generalisations about the whole population.
- ☐ Consider situations where statistics are misused and learn to evaluate the reliability and quality of data and data sources.
- ☐ Engage in discussions about the purpose of statistics and recognise misconceptions and misuses of statistics.
- ☐ Work with different types of data: categorical – nominal or ordinal numerical; discrete or continuous in order to clarify the problem at hand.
- ☐ Evaluate reliability of data and data sources.

Finding, collecting and organising data

- [ ] Formulate a statistics question based on data that vary allows for distinction between different types of data.
- [ ] Clarify the problem at hand.
- [ ] Formulate one (or more) questions that can be answered with data.
- [ ] Explore different ways of collecting data.
- [ ] Generate data, or source data, from other sources, including the internet.
- [ ] Select a sample from a population (Simple Random Sample).
- [ ] Recognise the importance of representativeness so as to avoid biased samples.
- [ ] Design a plan and collect data on the basis of above knowledge.
- [ ] Summarise data in diagrammatic form, including spreadsheets.

Representing data graphically and numerically

- [ ] Methods of representing data: Develop a sense that data can convey information and that organising data in different ways can help clarify what the data have to tell us.
- [ ] See a data set as a whole and be able to use fractions, quartiles and median to describe the data.

Graphically

- [ ] Select appropriate graphical or numerical methods to describe the sample (univariate data only).
- [ ] Evaluate the effectiveness of different displays in representing the findings of a statistical investigation conducted by others.
- [ ] Use pie charts, bar charts, line plots, histograms (equal intervals), stem and leaf plots and back-to-back stem and leaf plots to display data.
- [ ] Use appropriate graphical displays to compare data sets.
- [ ] Find that mean of a grouped frequency distribution.

Numerically

- [ ] Use a variety of summary statistics to describe the data: central tendency – mean, median, mode.
- [ ] Variability: range, quartiles and interquartile range
- [ ] Recognise the existence of outliers.

1 Coordinate Geometry of the Line

aims

- ☐ To know where to find the coordinate geometry formulae in the booklet of formulae and tables
- ☐ To learn how to apply these formulae to procedural and in-context examination questions
- ☐ To gain the ability, with practice, to recall and select the appropriate technique required by the exam questions

Coordinating the plane and plotting points

Coordinates are used to describe the **position** of a point on a plane (flat surface).

Two lines are drawn at right angles to each other.

The horizontal line is called the **x-axis**.

The vertical line is called the **y-axis**.

The two axes meet at a point called the **origin**.

The plane is called the **Cartesian** (kar-tee-zi-an) plane.

Every point on the plane has two coordinates, an **x-coordinate** and a **y-coordinate**.

The coordinates are enclosed in brackets.

The x-coordinate is always written first, then a comma, followed by the y-coordinate.

On the diagram, the coordinates of the point A are $(3, 2)$.

This is usually written as $A(3, 2)$.

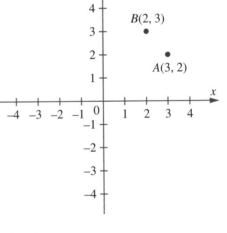

key point

- In a couple (x, y) the order is important
- The graph above shows that the point $A(3, 2)$ is different to the point $B(2, 3)$

The four quadrants

The intersecting x-axis and y-axis divide the plane into four regions called **quadrants**. These are numbered 1st, 2nd, 3rd and 4th, as shown on the right.

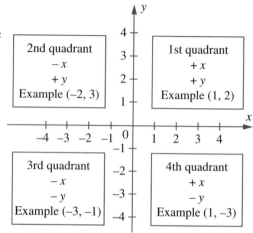

2nd quadrant
$-x$
$+y$
Example $(-2, 3)$

1st quadrant
$+x$
$+y$
Example $(1, 2)$

3rd quadrant
$-x$
$-y$
Example $(-3, -1)$

4th quadrant
$+x$
$-y$
Example $(1, -3)$

Example

Write down the coordinates of the points P, Q, R, S and T.

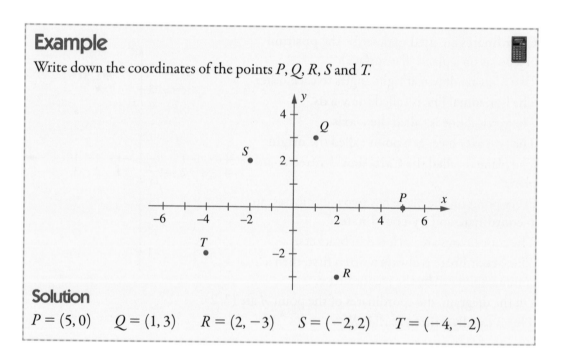

Solution

$P = (5, 0)$ $Q = (1, 3)$ $R = (2, -3)$ $S = (-2, 2)$ $T = (-4, -2)$

Translation

In mathematics, movement in a straight line is called a **translation**.

Under a translation, every point is moved the same distance in the same direction.

Example

Describe the translation that maps the points

(i) G to H

(ii) E to Q

(iii) R to D

Solution

(i) $G \rightarrow H$ is described by 2 units to the right and 5 units up.

This can be written as $\begin{pmatrix} 2 \\ 5 \end{pmatrix}$.

(ii) $E \rightarrow Q$ is described by 3 units to the left and

0 units up (or down). This can be written as $\begin{pmatrix} -3 \\ 0 \end{pmatrix}$.

(iii) $R \rightarrow D$ is described by 4 units to the right

and 5 units down. This can be written as $\begin{pmatrix} 4 \\ -5 \end{pmatrix}$.

key point

A more comprehensive treatment of translations can be found in Chapter 4 on transformation geometry.

Midpoint of a line segment

If (x_1, y_1) and (x_2, y_2) are two points, their midpoint is given by the formula:

$$\text{Midpoint} = \left(\frac{x_1 + x_2}{2}, \frac{y_1 + y_2}{2} \right)$$

(See booklet of formulae and tables page 18)

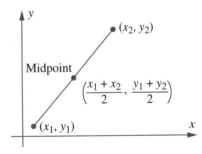

key point

Before using coordinate geometry formulae, always allocate one point to be (x_1, y_1) and the other to be (x_2, y_2).

Example

$A(8, 5)$ and $B(-10, 11)$ are two points. Find the midpoint of $[AB]$.

Solution

Midpoint formula $= \left(\dfrac{x_1 + x_2}{2}, \dfrac{y_1 + y_2}{2} \right)$

Let $(x_1, y_1) = (8, 5)$ and $(x_2, y_2) = (-10, 11)$

Midpoint $= \left(\dfrac{8 - 10}{2}, \dfrac{5 + 11}{2} \right) = \left(\dfrac{-2}{2}, \dfrac{16}{2} \right) = (-1, 8)$

In some questions, we will be given the midpoint and one end point of a line segment. We will be asked to find the other end point.

To find the other end point, use the following method:

1. Draw a rough diagram.
2. Find the translation that maps (moves) the given end point to the midpoint.
3. Apply the same translation to the midpoint to find the other end point.

Example

If $K(5, -3)$ is the midpoint of $[PQ]$ and $P = (4, 1)$, find the coordinates of Q.

Solution

1. Rough diagram:

$$P(4, 1) \qquad K(5, -3) \qquad Q(?, ?)$$

2. Translation from P to K, $\overrightarrow{PK}$. Rule: add 1 to x, subtract 4 from y.

This can be written as $\begin{pmatrix} 1 \\ -4 \end{pmatrix}$.

3. Apply this translation to K:

$$K(5, -3) \rightarrow (5 + 1, -3 - 4) = (6, -7)$$

$\therefore$ The coordinates of Q are $(6, -7)$.

Distance between two points

The given diagram shows the points $A(x_1, y_1)$ and $B(x_2, y_2)$.

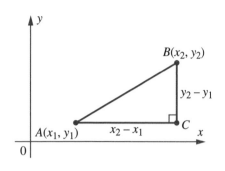

$|BC| = y_2 - y_1$ and $|AC| = x_2 - x_1$

Using the theorem of Pythagoras:

$$|AB|^2 = |AC|^2 + |BC|^2$$
$$= (x_2 - x_1)^2 + (y_2 - y_1)^2$$
$$\therefore \quad |AB| = \sqrt{(x_2 - x_1)^2 + (y_2 - y_1)^2}$$

The distance (length) between $A(x_1, y_1)$ and $B(x_2, y_2)$ is $|AB| = \sqrt{(x_2 - x_1)^2 + (y_2 - y_1)^2}$ (*See* booklet of formulae and tables page 18).

Example

Find the distance between the points $A(3, 2)$ and $B(5, -4)$.

Solution

Let $(x_1, y_1) = (3, 2)$ and $(x_2, y_2) = (5, -4)$

$$|AB| = \sqrt{(x_2 - x_1)^2 + (y_2 - y_1)^2}$$
$$= \sqrt{(5 - 3)^2 + (-4 - 2)^2}$$
$$= \sqrt{2^2 + (-6)^2}$$
$$= \sqrt{4 + 36}$$
$$= \sqrt{40}$$
$$= 2\sqrt{10}$$

At this stage the numbers are always positive.

ABCD is a rectangle with $A(3, 1)$ and $B(-3, 9)$. Given $|BC| = \frac{1}{5}|AB|$, calculate the area of ABCD.

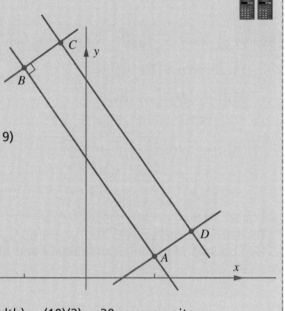

Solution:

Let $(x_1, y_1) = (3, 1)$ and $(x_2, y_2) = (-3, 9)$

$$|AB| = \sqrt{(x_2 - x_1)^2 + (y_2 - y_1)^2}$$
$$= \sqrt{(-3 - 3)^2 + (9 - 1)^2}$$
$$= \sqrt{(-6)^2 + (8)^2}$$
$$= \sqrt{36 + 64} = \sqrt{100} = 10$$

$$|BC| = \frac{1}{5}|AB| = \frac{1}{5}(10) = 2$$

Area rectangle ABCD = (length)(breadth) = (10)(2) = 20 square units

Henry the bee travels in a swarm from Zone A to Zone B.

The swarm's movement from zone A to zone B can be modelled by the translation that maps $(0, 0) \rightarrow (-1708, 503)$.

  (i) If Henry's starting position in the swarm in Zone A is $(1005, -98)$ find his position when the swarm moves to Zone B.

 (ii) Henry's best friend, Harriet, is also part of the swarm. If her position in Zone B is $(-711, 399)$, find her starting position.

(iii) Find the distance in cm between Henry and Harriet as they travel in the swarm when each unit is one mm.

Solution

(i) $(0, 0) \rightarrow (-1708, 503)$

   -1708 on the x-component

   $+503$ on the y-component

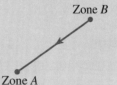
Zone B
Zone A

Henry: $(1005, -98) \rightarrow (1005 - 1708, -98 + 503) = (-703, 405)$

(ii) Harriet: $(?, ?) \rightarrow (-711, 399)$

Working backwards from Zone B to Zone A

   $+1708$ on the x-component

   -503 on the y-component.

Zone B
Zone A

Harriet's Zone A position $= (-711 + 1708, 399 - 503) = (997, -104)$

(iii) The distance between Henry and Harriet in the swarm is always the same. Hence, we can find the distance from:

Zone A. $(1005, -98)$ to $(997, -104)$ or   **Zone B.** $(-703, 405)$ to $(-711, 399)$

Here we find the distance from $(1005, -98)$ to $(997, -104)$.

Let $(x_1, y_1) = (1005, -98)$ and $(x_2, y_2) = (997, -104)$

$$\text{Distance} = \sqrt{(x_2 - x_1)^2 + (y_2 - y_1)^2}$$
$$= \sqrt{(997 - 1005)^2 + (-104 - (-98))^2}$$
$$= \sqrt{(-8)^2 + (-6)^2} = \sqrt{64 + 36} = \sqrt{100} = 10 \text{ units}$$

Since each unit is 1 mm

Then 10 units is 10 mm $=$ 1 cm

key point

As an exercise, you could verify that the distance from $(-711, 399)$ to $(-703, 405)$ is also 10 units = 1 cm.

exam Q

When geese fly in formation, they form an inverted v-shape.

(i) If the lines of geese can be represented by the equations
$2x + y - 11 = 0$ and $3x - 2y - 6 = 0$, find the coordinates of the leading goose.

After 1 hour, the leading goose has flown to a point $(37, 67)$.

(ii) Assuming the geese flew in a straight line and taking each unit to represent 1 km, find the distance travelled by the geese to the nearest km.

(iii) Hence, find the average flying speed in m/s.

Solution

(i) Solving the linear equations in two variables:

$$2x + y = 11 \quad ①$$
$$3x - 2y = 6 \quad ②$$
$$\overline{4x + 2y = 22} \quad ① \times 2$$
$$3x - 2y = 6 \quad ②$$
$$\overline{7x = 28} \quad \text{(Add)}$$
$$x = 4$$

Put $x = 4$ into ① or ②
$$2x + y = 11 \quad ①$$
$$\downarrow$$
$$2(4) + y = 11$$
$$8 + y = 11$$
$$y = 3$$

Solving linear equations is a skill you must know. Another example appears later in this chapter.

∴ The solution is $x = 4$ and $y = 3$ or $(4, 3)$

(ii) Use distance formula $= \sqrt{(x_2 - x_1)^2 + (y_2 - y_1)^2}$

Let $(x_1, y_1) = (4, 3)$ and $(x_2, y_2) = (37, 67)$

Distance $= \sqrt{(37 - 4)^2 + (67 - 3)^2} = \sqrt{1{,}089 + 4{,}096} = \sqrt{5{,}185}$

$= 72{\cdot}00694411$

Distance to nearest km $= 72$ km

(iii) Speed $= \dfrac{\text{Distance}}{\text{Time}} = \dfrac{72 \times 1{,}000}{60 \times 60} = 20$ m/sec

The exam may contain in-context questions at any stage. Be prepared to employ techniques learned elsewhere, as in the above question where

Speed $= \dfrac{\text{Distance}}{\text{Time}}$. This would seem to have no link to coordinate geometry.

Slope of a line

The slope of the line AB is defined as the

$$\frac{\text{vertical change}}{\text{horizontal change}} \quad \text{or} \quad \frac{\text{rise}}{\text{run}}$$

The slope of $AB = \dfrac{5}{10} = \dfrac{1}{2}$.

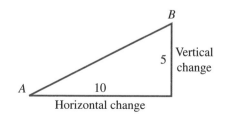

In the diagram on the right, the slope of *AB* is found by getting the

$$\frac{\text{vertical change}}{\text{horizontal change}} = \frac{y_2 - y_1}{x_2 - x_1}$$

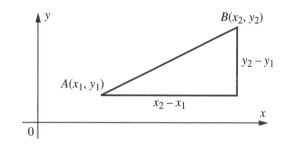

$$\text{Slope} = m = \frac{y_2 - y_1}{x_2 - x_1} \quad \textit{(See booklet of formulae and tables page 18)}$$

Positive and negative slopes

As we move from left to right the slope is positive if the line is rising and the slope is negative if the line is falling

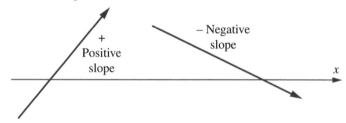

Example

Write down the slopes of the following lines in the diagram.

(i) GR (ii) BR

(iii) HJ (iv) GA

(v) AB (vi) BG

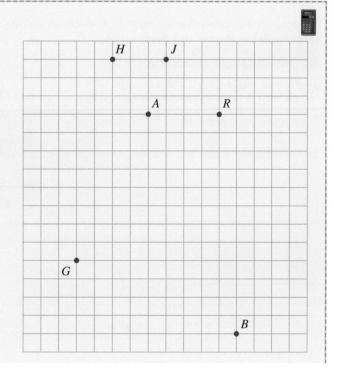

Solution

Use $\dfrac{\text{rise}}{\text{run}}$ (by counting the boxes) in each case to find

(i) Slope GR $= \dfrac{8}{8} = 1$ Line going up $\Rightarrow$ positive slope

(ii) Slope BR $= -\dfrac{12}{1} = -12$ Line going down $\Rightarrow$ negative slope

(iii) Slope HJ $= \dfrac{0}{3} = 0$ Horizontal line $\Rightarrow$ slope-zero

(iv) Slope GA $= \dfrac{8}{4} = 2$ Line going up $\Rightarrow$ positive slope

(v) Slope AB $= -\dfrac{12}{5}$ Line going down $\Rightarrow$ negative slope

(vi) Slope BG $= -\dfrac{4}{9}$ Line going down $\Rightarrow$ negative slope

exam
Q

An accountant plots the straight line value of a computer over a three-year period on the given graph.

(i) Find the slope of the line.

(ii) Hence write down the average rate of change in the value of the computer.

Justify your answer.

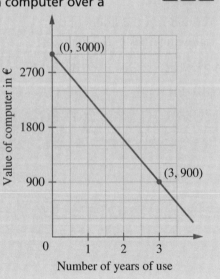

Solution

(i) Method 1

Using $\dfrac{\text{rise}}{\text{run}}$

$\dfrac{\text{rise}}{\text{run}} = \dfrac{\text{Down from 3000 to 900}}{\text{In 3 years}}$

$= \dfrac{-2100}{3}$

$= -700$

Method 2

Using $\dfrac{y_2 - y_1}{x_2 - x_1}$

$(x_1, y_1) = (0, 3000)$ and $(x_2, y_2) = (3, 900)$

$m = \dfrac{y_2 - y_1}{x_2 - x_1} = \dfrac{900 - 3000}{3 - 0} = \dfrac{-2100}{3}$

$m = -700$

Either method is accepted in this case.

The average rate of change $= m =$ the slope of the line.

(ii) The average rate of change is -700, which is a decrease in value of the computer by €700 per year.

Example

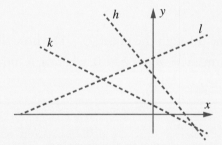

Which of the above lines k, h, or l has a positive slope? Justify your answer.

Solution

As we move from left to right, we observe l is the only line that is rising. Hence l is the only line with a positive slope.

From the diagram, we can see:

- The slope of the horizontal line p is zero.
- The slope of the vertical line q is not defined.

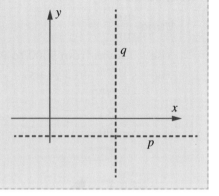

The equation of a line

The formula: $y - y_1 = m(x - x_1)$ (*See* booklet of formulae and tables page 18)

gives the equation of a line when we have:

- A point on the line (x_1, y_1)
- The slope of the line, m.

Example

Find the equation of the line through the point $(5, -1)$ whose slope is $\frac{2}{3}$.
Write your answer in the form $ax + by + c = 0$, where a, b and $c \in \mathbb{R}$.

Solution

$y - y_1 = m(x - x_1)$

$(x_1, y_1) = (5, -1)$ and $m = \dfrac{2}{3}$ are given in the question

$\therefore y - (-1) = \dfrac{2}{3}(x - 5)$

$y + 1 = \dfrac{2}{3}(x - 5)$

$3(y + 1) = 2(x - 5)$ Multiply both sides by 3 to remove the fraction

$3y + 3 = 2x - 10$

$-2x + 3y + 3 + 10 = 0$

$-2x + 3y + 13 = 0$

$2x - 3y - 13 = 0$

key
point

The formula cannot be used to get the equation of a vertical line since its slope is not defined. The equation of a vertical line is always $x =$ a constant.
This is covered in more detail later in this chapter.

exam
Q

The graph shows the cost of using a lecture theatre dependent on the number of attendees.

(i) What is the cost of a lecture theatre for 250 people?

(ii) Write down the slope of the line.

(iii) How does the slope help to calculate the extra cost if the number of attendees increases by 88.

(iv) Find the equation of the line.

(v) The graph does not start at (0, 0), the origin. Explain why this is to be expected.

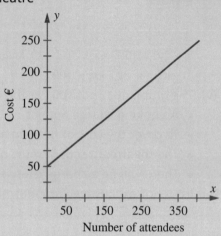

Solution

(i)

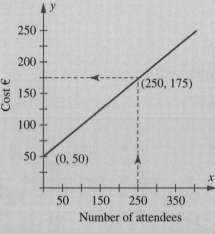

Reading from the graph
$\Rightarrow$ Cost of 250 attendees is €175

(ii) Slope of the line:

Method 1

$$\text{Slope} = \frac{y_2 - y_1}{x_2 - x_1}$$

Where $(x_1, y_1) = (0, 50)$

and $(x_2, y_2) = (250, 175)$

$$\text{Slope} = \frac{175 - 50}{250 - 0} = \frac{125}{250} = \frac{1}{2}$$

Method 2

$$\text{Slope} = \frac{\text{rise}}{\text{run}} = \frac{\text{up from 50 to 175}}{\text{up from 0 to 250}}$$

$$= \frac{+125}{+250}$$

$$= \frac{1}{2}$$

(iii) Slope $= \dfrac{1}{2} = \dfrac{\text{cost } €}{\text{number of attendees}}$

This indicates a rise of €1 for every 2 attendees, i.e. €0·5 for every extra attendee.

Hence an extra 88 attendees cost $€\dfrac{1}{2}$ each $= 88\left(\dfrac{1}{2}\right) = €44$.

(iv) Equation of the line

$m = \dfrac{1}{2}$ and $(x_1, y_1) = (0, 50)$

use $\quad y - y_1 = m(x - x_1)$

$\qquad y - 50 = \dfrac{1}{2}(x - 0)$

$\qquad 2y - 100 = x \qquad$ Multiply both sides by 2

$\qquad\quad 2y = x + 100$

(v) The graph does not start at the origin because:
- A booking charge applies.
- To cover the cost of heating and lighting.
- The theatre attendant must be paid to open and close the theatre.
- There will be a charge even if no one attends.

This list is not exhaustive. You may have a different answer.

The graphs below show the relationship between distances travelled and fuel consumption for John's car. The segments l_1 and l_2 represent the fuel consumption at steady speeds of 60 km/h and 100 km/h respectively.

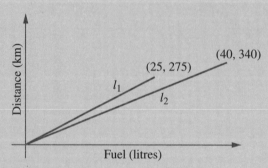

(a) Find the slopes of l_1 and l_2.

(b) What do these slopes tell you about the fuel consumption of the car at these speeds?

(c) Fuel costs 149·9 cent per litre. John drives a distance of 200 km at a steady speed. How much cheaper is the journey at 60 km/h than at 100 km/h?

Solution

(a) Slope $l_1 = \dfrac{\text{rise}}{\text{run}} = \dfrac{275}{25} = 11$ and   Slope $l_2 = \dfrac{\text{rise}}{\text{run}} = \dfrac{340}{40} = 8{\cdot}5$

(b) Speed 60 km/hour is associated with the slope of $l_1 = 11$

Speed 100 km/hour is associated with the slope of $l_2 = 8{\cdot}5$

The higher slope for l_1 indicates that you get more km/litre at the lower speed. Or you could state that more fuel is used at the higher speed.

(c) l_1 gets 11 km for 1 litre

l_1 gets 1 km for $\dfrac{1}{11}$ litre

l_1 gets 200 km for $\dfrac{200}{11}$ litres

l_1 gets 200 km for 18·18 litres

l_2 gets 8·5 km for 1 litre

l_2 gets 1 km for $\dfrac{1}{8{\cdot}5}$ litre

l_2 gets 200 km for $\dfrac{200}{8{\cdot}5}$ litres

l_2 gets 200 km for 23·53 litres

$\Rightarrow$ 23·53 − 18·18 = 5·35 litres less fuel consumed at the lower speed.

$\therefore$ 5·35 × 149·9 cent = 801·965 cent cheaper at the lower speed.

Answer: 802 cent or €8·02.

exam focus

This question was awarded 15 marks in total.

14 marks were awarded if **either** part (a) or part (c) were fully correct.

Part (b) was awarded 7 marks if the other two parts were not attempted.

Watch your time budget. Attempt every part of every question.

The slope of a line when given its equation

To find the slope of a line when given its equation, do the following:

Method 1:

> Rearrange the equation to get y on its own, then the number in front of x is the slope.

Note: The number in front of x is called the **coefficient** of x.

The number on its own is called the y **intercept**.

In short: write the line in the form $y = mx + c$.

$$y = mx \quad\quad + \quad\quad\quad\quad c \quad \text{(\textit{See} booklet of formulae and tables page 18)}$$
$$\downarrow \quad\quad\quad\quad\quad\quad\quad\quad \downarrow$$
$$y = (\text{slope})x \quad + \quad (\text{where the line cuts the } y\text{-axis})$$

Method 2:

> If the line is in the form $ax + by + c = 0$, then $-\dfrac{a}{b}$ is the slope.

In words: slope $= -\dfrac{\text{number in front of } x}{\text{number in front of } y}$

Note: When using this method, make sure every term is on the left-hand side in the given equation of the line.

Example

Write down the slope, m, of each of the following lines:

(i) $y = 4x - 3$ (ii) $y = 8 - 2x$ (iii) $y = x + 5$

(iv) $2y = 7x - 10$ (v) $y - 6x = 0$ (vi) $3y + 2x + 12 = 0$

Solution

Using $y = mx + c$ in each case:

(i) $y = 4x - 3 \Rightarrow m = 4$

(ii) $y = 8 - 2x \Rightarrow m = -2$ (Be careful to include the minus)

(iii) $y = x + 5 \Rightarrow m = 1$ (m not zero)

(iv) $2y = 7x - 10$ (Divide each term by 2)

$$y = \frac{7}{2}x - 5 \Rightarrow m = \frac{7}{2}$$

(v) $y - 6x = 0$

$$y = 6x \Rightarrow m = 6$$

(vi) $3y + 2x + 12 = 0$

$$3y = -2x - 12 \quad\quad\quad \text{(Divide each term by 3)}$$

$$y = \frac{-2}{3}x - 4 \Rightarrow m = \frac{-2}{3}$$

The bigger the value of *m* (positive or negative) the steeper the line.

Parallel lines

To prove whether or not two lines are parallel, do the following:

1. Find the slope of each line.

2. (a) If the slopes are the same, the lines are parallel.

   (b) If the slopes are different, the lines are **not** parallel.

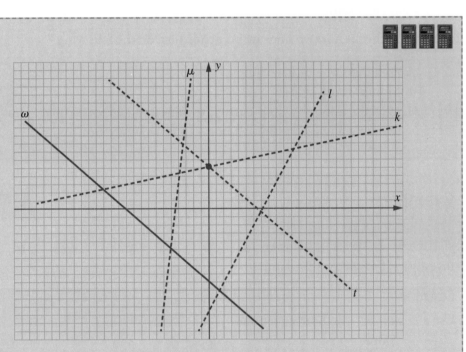

Five lines μ, ω, t, l and k in the coordinate plane are shown in the diagram above.

The slopes of the five lines are given in the table.

Complete the table, matching the lines to their slopes.

Two lines have slope $-\dfrac{9}{10}$. This means two lines are parallel.

$\therefore$ t has slope $-\dfrac{9}{10}$ and ω has slope $-\dfrac{9}{10}$.

Slope	Line
$\frac{1}{6}$	
$\frac{5}{3}$	
$-\frac{9}{10}$	
13	
$-\frac{9}{10}$	

Solution

l, *k* and *μ* all have positive slopes (because they are all rising).

By observation, *μ* has the steepest positive slope.

∴ *μ* has slope 13.

Also by observation, *k* has the least steep positive slope.

∴ *k* has slope $\frac{1}{6}$.

Since the only remaining line is *l* and the only remaining slope

is $\frac{5}{3}$ ⇒ *l* has slope $\frac{5}{3}$.

Slop	Line
$\frac{1}{6}$	*k*
$\frac{5}{3}$	
$-\frac{9}{10}$	*t*
13	*μ*
$-\frac{9}{10}$	*ω*

Perpendicular lines

To prove whether or not two lines are perpendicular, do the following:

1. Find the slope of each line.
2. Multiply both slopes.
3. (a) If the answer in step 2 is −1, the lines are perpendicular.
   (b) If the answer in step 2 is **not** −1, the lines are **not** perpendicular.

Example

The equation of two lines are:

p: $10x + 4y - 9 = 0$ and *q*: $2x - 5y + 20 = 0$

Investigate if *p* is perpendicular to *q*.

Solution

Use $y = mx + c$ on both equations

Slope of *p*	Slope of *q*
$10x + 4y - 9 = 0$	$2x - 5y + 20 = 0$
$4y = -10x + 9$	$-5y = -2x - 20$
(Divide each term by 4)	$5y = 2x + 20$ (Divide each term by 5)
$y = -\frac{10}{4}x + \frac{9}{4}$	$y = \frac{2}{5}x + 4$
∴ *p* has slope $= -\frac{10}{4} = -\frac{5}{2}$	∴ *q* has slope $= \frac{2}{5}$

$$\text{(slope of } p) \times \text{(slope of } q) = -\frac{5}{2} \times \frac{2}{5} = -1$$

Hence line *p* is perpendicular to line *q*.

To verify that a point belongs to a line

To verify that a point belongs to a line, substitute the coordinates of the point into the equation of the line. If the coordinates satisfy the equation, then the point is on the line. Otherwise, the point is **not** on the line.

Example

Investigate if the points $(-2, 9)$ and $(-5, 3)$ are on the line $5x - 3y + 34 = 0$.

Solution

$(-2, 9)$ $5x - 3y + 34 = 0$

Substitute $x = -2$ and $y = 9$

$5(-2) - 3(9) + 34$

$= -10 - 27 + 34$

$= -37 + 34$

$= -3 \neq 0$

Does not satisfy the equation

$\therefore$ $(-2, 9)$ is not on the line.

$(-5, 3)$ $5x - 3y + 34 = 0$

Substitute $x = -5$ and $y = 3$

$5(-5) - 3(3) + 34$

$= -25 - 9 + 34$

$= -34 + 34$

$= 0$

Satisfies the equation

$\therefore$ $(-5, 3)$ is on the line.

Example

(i) The point $(k, -2)$ is on the line $4x + 3y - 14 = 0$. Find the value of k.

(ii) The point $(1, 2)$ is on the line $3x + ty - 11 = 0$. Find the value of t.

Solution

(i) $4x + 3y - 14 = 0$

Substitute $x = k$ and $y = -2$

$(k, -2): 4(k) + 3(-2) - 14 = 0$

$4k - 6 - 14 = 0$

$4k - 20 = 0$

$4k = 20$

$k = 5$

(ii) $3x + ty - 11 = 0$

Substitute $x = 1$ and $y = 2$

$(1, 2): 3(1) + t(2) - 11 = 0$

$3 + 2t - 11 = 0$

$2t - 8 = 0$

$2t = 8$

$t = 4$

Graphing lines

To draw a line, only two points are needed. The easiest points to find are where lines cut the x- and y-axes. This is known as the **intercept method**.

On the x-axis, $y = 0$. On the y-axis, $x = 0$.

To draw a line, do the following:

1. Let $y = 0$ and find x.
2. Let $x = 0$ and find y.
3. Plot these two points.
4. Draw the line through these points.

If the constant in the equation of a line is zero, e.g. $3x - 5y = 0$, or $4x = 3y$, then the line will pass through the origin, $(0, 0)$. In this case the **intercept method** will not work.

To draw a line that contains the origin, $(0, 0)$, do the following:

1. Choose a suitable value for x and find the corresponding value for y (or vice versa).
2. Plot this point.
3. A line drawn through this point and the origin is the required line.

A very suitable method is to let x equal the number in front of y and then find the corresponding value for y (or vice versa).

Example

Graph the line $3x + 4y = 0$.

Solution

1. Let $x = 4$ (number in front of y).

$$3x + 4y = 0$$
$$\downarrow$$
$$3(4) + 4y = 0$$
$$12 + 4y = 0$$
$$4y = -12$$
$$y = -3$$

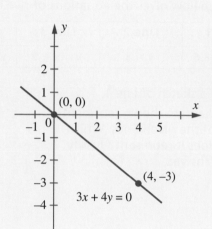

2. Plot the point $(4, -3)$.
3. Draw the line through the points $(4, -3)$ and $(0, 0)$.

Lines parallel to the axes

$x = 2$ is a line parallel to the y-axis through 2 on the x-axis. $y = -1$ is a line parallel to the x-axis through -1 on the y-axis.

key point

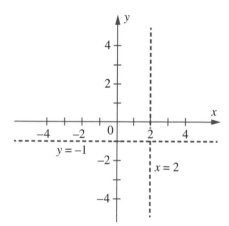

$y = 0$ is the equation of the x-axis.
$x = 0$ is the equation of the y-axis.

exam focus

All horizontal lines (parallel to x-axis) have an angle of inclination of 0°, meaning their slopes are zero.

All vertical lines (parallel to y-axis) have an angle of inclination of 90°, meaning their slopes are infinitely steep.

The table below gives the equations of five lines.

Line 1	Line 2	Line 3	Line 4	Line 5
$y = 3x - 6$	$y = 3$	$y = x - 7$	$y = -2x + 4$	$y = 4x - 16$

(i) Draw a sketch of line 1.

(ii) The diagram shown represents one of the given lines. Which line does it represent? Justify your answer.

(iii) The table shows some values of x and y for the equation of one of the lines. Which equation do they satisfy? Show your work.

x	7	9	10
y	12	20	24

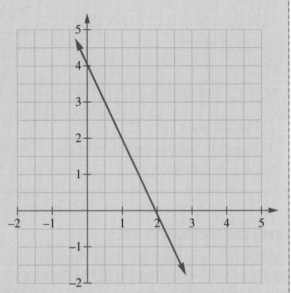

Solution

(i) Line 1 is $y = 3x - 6$

Let $y = 0 \Rightarrow y = 3x - 6$
$$0 = 3x - 6$$
$$6 = 3x$$
$$2 = x$$
$(2, 0) \in$ Line 1

Let $x = 0 \Rightarrow y = 3x - 6$
$$y = 3(0) - 6$$
$$y = 0 - 6$$
$$y = -6$$
$(0, -6) \in$ Line 1

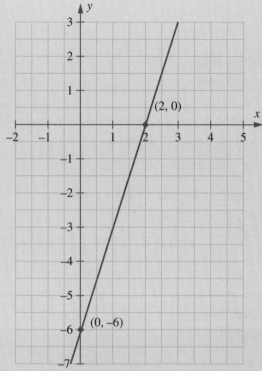

(ii) Line 4 is $y = -2x + 4$. It has a slope of -2.

It is the only line with a negative (decreasing slope). Hence line 4 matches the given diagram.

(iii) Check for $x = 7$ in each of the given lines and verify the value for $y = 12$,

Line 1: $y = 3x - 6 \Rightarrow y = 3(7) - 6 = 21 - 6 = 15 \neq 12$

Line 2: $y = 3$ is never $= 12$

Line 3: $y = x - 7 \Rightarrow y = 7 - 7$
$= 0 \neq 12$

Line 4: $y = -2x + 4 \Rightarrow y$
$= -2(7) + 4 = -14 + 4$
$= -10 \neq 12$

Line 5: $y = 4x - 16 \Rightarrow y = 4(7) - 16$
$= 28 - 16 = 12 = 12$

As line 5 is the only one to satisfy
the point (7, 12), line 5 is our answer.

If $x = 7 \Rightarrow y = 12$ worked for more than one of the given lines, we would continue by taking $x = 9 \Rightarrow y = 20$ from the given table and the correct answer would be the line that satisfies both conditions.

$P(-1, 2)$ and $R(3, 4)$ are two points.

(i) Find Q the midpoint of $[PR]$.

(ii) Find the slope of PR.

(iii) Find the equation of the line l, the perpendicular bisector of $[PR]$.

(iv) The equation of the line k is $x - 2y = 0$.

Find W, the point of intersection of l and k.

Solution:

Let $(x_1, y_1) = (-1, 2)$ and $(x_2, y_2) = (3, 4)$

(i) $Q = \left(\dfrac{x_1 + x_2}{2}, \dfrac{y_1 + y_2}{2}\right) = \left(\dfrac{-1 + 3}{2}, \dfrac{2 + 4}{2}\right) = \left(\dfrac{2}{2}, \dfrac{6}{2}\right) = (1, 3)$

(ii) Slope $PR = m = \dfrac{y_2 - y_1}{x_2 - x_1} = \dfrac{4 - 2}{3 - (-1)} = \dfrac{2}{3 + 1} = \dfrac{2}{4} = \dfrac{1}{2}$

(iii) For perpendicular lines

(Slope of PR) $\times$ (slope l) $= -1$

$\left(\dfrac{1}{2}\right) \times$ (slope l) $= -1$

$\qquad$ Slope $l = -2$ $\qquad$ Multiply both sides by 2

Equation of l is given by

$\quad y - y_1 = m(x - x_1)$

Where $m = -2$ and $(x, y,) = Q = (1, 3)$:

$\quad y - 3 = -2(x - 1)$

$\quad y - 3 = -2x + 2$

$\qquad y = -2x + 5$

$\quad y + 2x = 5$

(iv) To find $l \cap k$:

$y + 2x = 5$	①	
$x - 2y = 0$	②	
$2y + 4x = 10$	① × 2	
$-2y + x = 0$	② rearrange	
$5x = 10$	(Add)	
$x = 2$		

Put $x = 2$ into ① or ②

$\quad y + 2x = 5$ $\quad$ ①

$\quad y + 2(2) = 5$

$\quad y + 4 = 5$

$\qquad y = 1$

$\therefore W = (2, 1) = l \cap k$

Given the point $(3, -4)$ is on the line l: $7x - 2y - 29 = 0$,
find the equation of the image of l under the translation $(0, 2) \rightarrow (-1, 5)$.

Solution

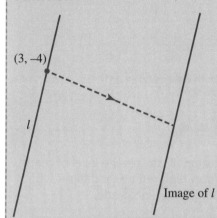

(3, –4)

l

Image of l

$(0, 2) \rightarrow (-1, 5)$ may be written as $\begin{pmatrix} -1 \\ 3 \end{pmatrix}$.

Rule: Subtract 1 from x, add 3 to y.
$\therefore (3, -4) \rightarrow (3 - 1, -4 + 3) = (2, -1)$

key point

A translation maps a line onto a parallel line.

Since parallel lines have equal slopes, the image of l has the form:
$$7x - 2y + k = 0 \quad \text{where } k \in \mathbb{R}$$
We know $(2, -1) \in 7x - 2y + k = 0$
$$\therefore 7(2) - 2(-1) + k = 0$$
$$14 + 2 + k = 0$$
$$16 + k = 0$$
$$k = -16$$
Equation of image of l: $7x - 2y - 16 = 0$

g is the line containing the points
$A(-1, 7)$ and $B(p, 4)$ as in the diagram.
Given the line g is parallel to the line
h with equation $2y = 3x - 10$, find the
value of p.

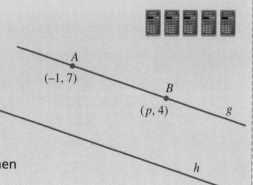

A
$(-1, 7)$
B
$(p, 4)$
g
h

Solution

Let $(x_1, y_1) = (-1, 7)$ and $(x_2, y_2) = (p, 4)$ then

slope of $g = \dfrac{y_2 - y_1}{x_2 - x_1} = \dfrac{4 - 7}{p - (-1)} = \dfrac{-3}{p + 1}$

Slope of $2y = 3x - 10$ is given by $y = \dfrac{3}{2}x - 5$ (Divide by 2)

$$\Rightarrow m = \frac{3}{2}$$

Since parallel lines have equal slopes,

    slope of line g = slope of line h

$$\frac{-3}{p + 1} = \frac{3}{2}$$

$(2)(-3) = (3)(p + 1)$ Multiply both sides by (2) $(p + 1)$

$-6 = 3p + 3$

$-9 = 3p$

$-3 = p$

This solution illustrates the level of maths application required by candidates who are aiming for a high grade.

Given the points on the diagram:

B	C	E	F
(2, 0)	(−4, −4)	(−6, 0)	(4, −4)

(i) Find **(a)** $|BE|$ **(b)** $|CF|$.

(ii) Find the slope of **(a)** EC **(b)** BF.

(iii) What is the ratio of the area of the triangle BCE to the area of the triangle BCF?
Justify your answer.

(iv) Prove that the triangle BCE is congruent to the triangle BCF.

Solution

(i) By observation from the diagram **(a)** $|BE| = 8$ **(b)** $|CF| = 8$

(ii) Use $m = \dfrac{y_2 - y_1}{x_2 - x_1}$ on both parts

(a) $(x_1, y_1) = (-6, 0)$ E
           $(x_2, y_2) = (-4, -4)$ C

$$m = \frac{-4 - 0}{-4 - (-6)} = \frac{-4}{-4 + 6}$$

$$m = \frac{-4}{2} = -2$$

(b) $(x_1, y_1) = (2, 0)$ B
     $(x_2, y_2) = (4, -4)$ F

$$m = \frac{-4 - 0}{4 - 2} = \frac{-4}{2} = -2$$

The slopes of EC and BF are equal. This tells us that EC is parallel to BF. This will be very useful in part **(iv)** of this question.

(iii) Use the area $\Delta = \dfrac{1}{2}$ (base) (perpendicular height) on both

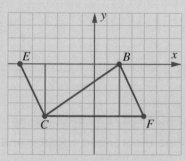

Area $\Delta BCF = \dfrac{1}{2}|CF|$ ($\perp$ height)

$= \dfrac{1}{2}(8)(4)$

$= 16$ square units

Area $\Delta BCE = \dfrac{1}{2}|BE|$ ($\perp$ height)

$= \dfrac{1}{2}(8)(4)$

$= 16$ square units

Ratio $\Rightarrow \dfrac{\text{Area } \Delta BCE}{\text{Area } \Delta BCF} = \dfrac{16}{16} = \dfrac{1}{1} = 1$

The above work is the justification.

(iv) Slope $EB =$ Slope $CF = 0$ $\therefore$ EB parallel to CF from part **(ii)** EC parallel to BF

Hence $BFCE$ is a parallelogram.

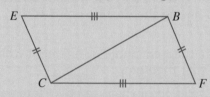

An earlier part of an exam question will often help answer a (more difficult) later part. Watch out for this.

Now consider ΔBCE and ΔBCF:

$|BC| = |BC|$ same

$\left.\begin{array}{l} |EC| = |BF| \\ |EB| = |CF| \end{array}\right\}$ opposite sides of a parallelogram

Hence (By SSS), ΔBCE is congruent (identical) to ΔBCF

Part **(iv)** above is an excellent example of an exam question linking two topics on our course. In this case, coordinate geometry is linked with Euclidean geometry.

aims

☐ To know the definitions of the geometry terms listed in the glossary below

☐ To know all theorems, corollaries and axioms

☐ To be able to reproduce the proofs for theorems 4, 6, 9, 14 and 19

☐ To be able to solve problems applying the theorems, corollaries and axioms

Glossary of terms

GLOSSARY OF EXAMINABLE TERMS

Axiom: An axiom is a statement which is assumed to be true. It can be accepted without a proof and used as a basis for an argument.

Converse: The converse of a theorem is formed by taking the conclusion as the starting point and having the starting point as the conclusion.

Corollary: A corollary follows after a theorem and is a statement which must be true because of that theorem.

Implies: Implies indicates a logical relationship between two statements, such that if the first is true then the second must be true.

Is congruent to: Two things are said to be congruent if they are identical in size and shape.

Proof: A proof is a sequence of statements (made up of axioms, assumptions and arguments) these follow logically from the preceding one, starting at an axiom or previously proven theorem and ending with the statement of the theorem to be proven.

Theorem: A theorem is a statement which has been proved to be true, deduced from axioms by logical argument.

You are required to know the following axioms, theorems and corollaries and must be able to apply them in answering questions in geometry.

Axioms

Axiom 1: There is exactly one line through any two given points.

Axiom 2: Ruler axiom

The distance between points P and Q has the following properties:

1. The distance $|PQ|$ is never negative.

2. The distance between two points is the same, whether we measure from P to Q or from Q to P.

3. If there exists some point R between P and Q, then the distance from P to Q is equal to the sum of the distances from P to R and R to Q.

$$|PR| + |RQ| = |PQ|$$

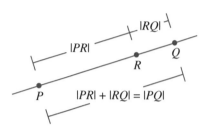

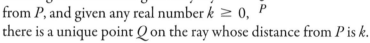

4. A ray is a line which starts at one point and continues in a certain direction forever.

Marking off a distance: given any ray from P, and given any real number $k \geq 0$, there is a unique point Q on the ray whose distance from P is k.

Axiom 3: Protractor axiom

The number of degrees in an angle (also known as its degree-measure) is always a number between 0° and 360°. Angles have the following properties:

1. A straight angle has 180°.

2. If we know the angle $A°$, opened up at a point P, then there are two possible rays from P that form that angle as shown in the diagram.

3. If an angle is divided into two, then that angle is equal to the sum of the two angles that make it up.

$$|\angle QPR| = |\angle QPS| + |\angle SPR|$$
$$|\angle QPR| = A° + B°$$

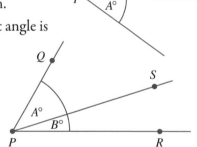

Axiom 4: Congruent triangles

We can say that two triangles are congruent if:

1. SAS: Two sides and the angle in between are the same in both.

2. ASA: Two angles and a side are the same in both.

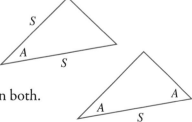

3. SSS: All three sides are the same in both.

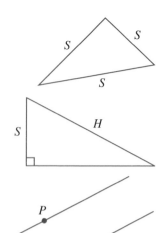

4. RHS: The right angle, hypotenuse and another side are the same in both.

Axiom 5: Given any line *l* and a point *P*, there is exactly one line through *P* that is parallel to *l*.

Theorems

- The application of all theorems can be examined.

- Only proofs for theorems 4, 6, 9, 14 and 19 are examinable (marked with an asterisk).

- You will be presented with the worded statement of a theorem, without reference to the theorem number.

- Proofs are expected to begin with a diagram, followed by the following headings: 'Given', 'To prove', 'Construction' and 'Proof'.

- You must explain all construction steps fully.

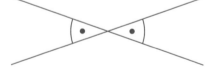

key point

Theorems 7, 8, 16, 17 and 18 are **not** on your course.

Theorem 1: **Vertically opposite angles**

Vertically opposite angles are equal in measure.

Theorem 2: **Isosceles triangles**

1. In an isosceles triangle, the angles opposite the equal sides are equal.
2. The converse states that, if two angles are equal, then the triangle is isosceles.

Theorem 3: **Alternate angles**

If a transversal makes equal alternate angles on two lines, then the lines are parallel (and converse).
Note: arrows are used to indicate parallel lines

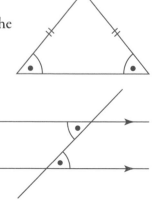

***Theorem 4:* Angles in a triangle**

The angles in any triangle add to 180°.

$$A° + B° + C° = 180°$$

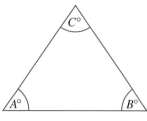

***Theorem 5:* Corresponding angles**

Two lines are parallel if, and only if, for any transversal, the corresponding angles are equal.

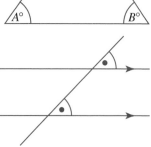

***Theorem 6:* Exterior angle**

Each exterior angle of a triangle is equal to the sum of the interior opposite angles.

$$E° = A° + B°$$

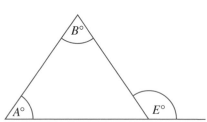

***Theorem 9:* Parallelograms**

In a parallelogram, opposite sides are equal and opposite angles are equal.
Two converses of this theorem are true:

1. If the opposite angles of a quadrilateral are equal, then it is a parallelogram.

2. If the opposite sides of a quadrilateral are equal, then it is a parallelogram.

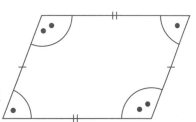

Corollary: A diagonal divides a parallelogram into two congruent triangles.

***Theorem 10:* Diagonals of a parallelogram**

The diagonals of a parallelogram bisect each other.

Converse:

If the diagonals of a quadrilateral bisect one another, then it is a parallelogram.

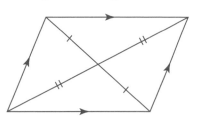

***Theorem 11:* Transversals**

If three parallel lines cut off equal segments on some transversal line, then they will cut off equal segments on any other transversal.

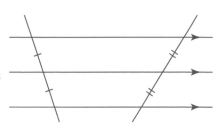

Theorem 12: Proportional sides

Let ABC be a triangle. If a line XY is parallel to BC and cuts $[AB]$ in the ratio $s:t$, then it also cuts $[AC]$ in the same ratio.

Converse:

If a line XY cuts the sides AB and AC in the same ratio, then it is parallel to BC.

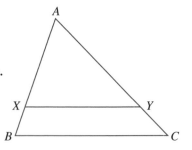

Theorem 13: Similar triangles

If two triangles are similar, then their sides are proportional, in order.

$$\frac{|PQ|}{|AB|} = \frac{|PR|}{|AC|} = \frac{|QR|}{|BC|}$$

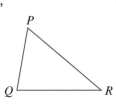 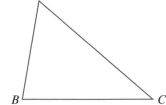

Converse:

If the corresponding sides of two triangles are proportional, then they are similar.

*Theorem 14: Theorem of Pythagoras

In a right-angled triangle, the square of the hypotenuse is the sum of the squares of the other two sides.

$$|AC|^2 = |AB|^2 + |BC|^2$$

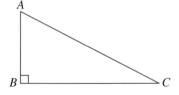

Theorem 15: Converse to Pythagoras

If the square of one side is the sum of the squares of the other two, then the angle opposite the first side is a right angle.

*Theorem 19: Circle theorem

The angle at the centre of a circle standing on a given arc is twice the angle at any point of the circle standing on the same arc.

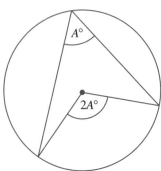

Corollary 1:   All angles at points of a circle standing on the same arc are equal.

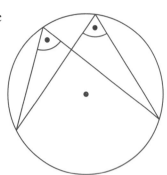

Corollary 2:   Each angle in a semicircle is a right angle.

Corollary 3:   If the angle standing on a chord $[BC]$ at some point on the circle is a right angle, then $[BC]$ is a diameter.

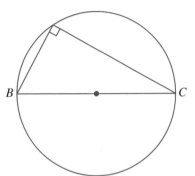

Corollary 4:   If $ABCD$ is a cyclic quadrilateral, then opposite angles sum to 180°.

$$A° + C° = 180°$$
$$B° + D° = 180°$$

Converse:

If the opposite angles of a quadrilateral sum to 180°, the quadrilateral is cyclic.

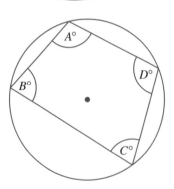

When solving questions which involve diagrams, it is often helpful to do rough copies, in pencil, of the diagram on a separate piece of paper. This allows you to mark things on the diagram and to try different approaches, **without drawing on the original image**. This can be useful if you take the wrong approach the first time. You still have a clean diagram to work from.

Proof of theorems

You must be able to reproduce the proofs for theorems 4, 6, 9, 14 and 19.

Theorem 4: The three angles in any triangle add to 180°.

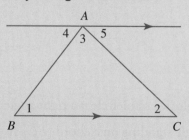

Given:	$\triangle ABC$ with angles 1, 2 and 3
To prove:	$\lvert\angle 1\rvert + \lvert\angle 2\rvert + \lvert\angle 3\rvert = 180°$
Construction:	Draw a line through A, parallel to BC. Label angles 4 and 5.
Proof:	$\lvert\angle 1\rvert = \lvert\angle 4\rvert$ and $\lvert\angle 2\rvert = \lvert\angle 5\rvert$ (Alternate angles)

$\therefore \quad \lvert\angle 1\rvert + \lvert\angle 2\rvert + \lvert\angle 3\rvert = \lvert\angle 4\rvert + \lvert\angle 5\rvert + \lvert\angle 3\rvert$

but $\lvert\angle 4\rvert + \lvert\angle 5\rvert + \lvert\angle 3\rvert = 180°$ (Straight angle)

$\therefore \quad \lvert\angle 1\rvert + \lvert\angle 2\rvert + \lvert\angle 3\rvert = 180°$

Theorem 6: Each exterior angle of a triangle is equal to the sum of the two interior opposite angles.

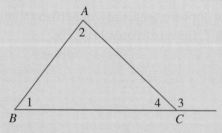

Given:	$\triangle ABC$ with interior opposite angles 1 and 2 and exterior angle 3
To prove:	$\lvert\angle 1\rvert + \lvert\angle 2\rvert = \lvert\angle 3\rvert$
Construction:	Label angle 4.
Proof:	$\lvert\angle 1\rvert + \lvert\angle 2\rvert + \lvert\angle 4\rvert = 180°$ (Three angles in a triangle)

$\lvert\angle 3\rvert + \lvert\angle 4\rvert = 180°$ (Straight angle)

$\therefore \quad \lvert\angle 1\rvert + \lvert\angle 2\rvert + \lvert\angle 4\rvert = \lvert\angle 3\rvert + \lvert\angle 4\rvert$

$\therefore \quad \lvert\angle 1\rvert + \lvert\angle 2\rvert = \lvert\angle 3\rvert$

Theorem 9: In a parallelogram, opposite sides are equal and opposite angles are equal.

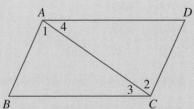

Given:	Parallelogram $ABCD$
To prove:	$|AB| = |DC|, |AD| = |BC|$
	$|\angle ABC| = |\angle ADC|, |\angle BAD| = |\angle BCD|$
Construction:	Join A to C.
	Label angles 1, 2, 3 and 4.
Proof:	Consider $\triangle ABC$ and $\triangle ADC$:

$|\angle 1| = |\angle 2|$ and $|\angle 3| = |\angle 4|$ (Alternate angles)

$|AC| = |AC|$ (Common side)

$\therefore \ \triangle ABC \equiv \triangle ADC$ (ASA)

$\therefore \ |AB| = |DC|$ and $|AD| = |BC|$ (Corresponding sides)

and $|\angle ABC| = |\angle ADC|$ (Corresponding angles)

Similarly, $|\angle BAD| = |\angle BCD|$

Theorem 14: Theorem of Pythagoras: In a right-angled triangle, the square of the hypotenuse is the sum of the squares of the other two sides.

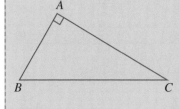 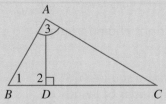 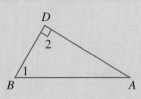

Given:	$\triangle ABC, |\angle BAC| = 90°$
To prove:	$|BC|^2 = |AB|^2 + |AC|^2$
Construction:	Draw $AD \perp BC$.
	Label angles 1, 2 and 3.
Proof:	In $\triangle$s ABC and DBA:

$|\angle 1| = |\angle 1|$ (Common angle)

$|\angle 2| = |\angle 3| = 90°$ (Construction)

$\therefore$ $\triangle ABC$ and $\triangle DBA$ are similar.

$\therefore$ $\dfrac{|AB|}{|BC|} = \dfrac{|BD|}{|AB|}$ (Corresponding sides are in proportion)

$\therefore$ $|AB|^2 = |BC| \times |BD|$ ①   (Cross-multiply)

Similarly, $\triangle ABC$ and $\triangle DAC$ are similar.

And $|AC|^2 = |BC| \times |DC|$ ②

Adding ① and ②:

$|AB|^2 + |AC|^2 = |BC| \times |BD| + |BC| \times |DC|$

$\qquad\qquad\qquad = |BC|(|BD| + |DC|)$ (Factorise out $|BC|$)

$\qquad\qquad\qquad = |BC| \times |BC|$

$\qquad\qquad\qquad = |BC|^2$

$\therefore$ $|BC|^2 = |AB|^2 + |AC|^2$

Alternative proof for Theorem 14:

Theorem 14: Theorem of Pythagoras: In a right-angled triangle, the square of the hypotenuse is the sum of the squares of the other two sides.

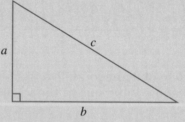

Given:	A right angled triangle
To prove:	$a^2 + b^2 = c^2$
Construction:	Draw a square *PQRS* with sides of length $a + b$.
	Draw four congruent right-angled triangles in the square with sides of length a and b and hypotenuse c, as shown.
	Label angles 1, 2, 3 and 4.

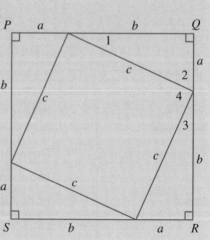

Proof: Each of the four inscribed triangles is congruent to the original triangle (*SAS*).

∴ Each side of the inner quadrilateral has length *c*.

$$|\angle 1| + |\angle 2| = 90° \quad \text{(Remaining angles in the triangle)}$$

$$|\angle 1| = |\angle 3| \quad \text{(Corresponding angles in congruent triangles)}$$

$$\therefore |\angle 2| + |\angle 3| = 90°$$

$$\therefore |\angle 4| = 90° \quad \text{(Straight angle)}$$

∴ The inscribed quadrilateral is a square.

Area of square *PQRS* = 4 (Area of one triangle + area of inscribed square)

$$(a + b)^2 = 4\left(\tfrac{1}{2}ab\right) + c^2$$

$$a^2 + 2ab + b^2 = 2ab + c^2$$

$$\therefore \qquad a^2 + b^2 = c^2 \qquad \text{(Subtract 2ab from both sides)}$$

key point

A difficulty with the previous proof is trying to draw the diagram. To make it easier let $a = 2$ cm, $b = 5$ cm and draw a square with each side 7 cm in length. Then simply mark off 2 cm on each side in a clockwise direction. Join these points to construct the smaller square.

Theorem 19: The angle at the centre of a circle standing on a given arc is twice the angle at any point of the circle standing on the same arc.

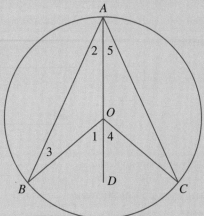

Given:	Circle, centre *O*, containing points *A*, *B* and *C*
To prove:	$|\angle BOC| = 2|\angle BAC|$
Construction:	Join *A* to *O* and continue to *D*.
	Label angles 1, 2, 3, 4 and 5.

Proof:

Consider $\triangle AOB$:

$|\angle 1| = |\angle 2| + |\angle 3|$ (Exterior angle of $\triangle AOB$)

But $|\angle 2| = |\angle 3|$ ($|OA| = |OB|$: both radii)

$\therefore$ $|\angle 1| = 2|\angle 2|$

Similarly, $|\angle 4| = 2|\angle 5|$

$\therefore |\angle 1| + |\angle 4| = 2|\angle 2| + 2|\angle 5|$

$\therefore |\angle 1| + |\angle 4| = 2(|\angle 2| + |\angle 5|)$

i.e. $|\angle BOC| = 2|\angle BAC|$

Application and use of theorems

You must know all of the theorems very well and be able to apply them when solving problems in geometry.

key point

- Be aware that there may be more than one method of proof for answering questions by the application of theorems.
- Many geometry problems will involve aspects of trigonometry.

Finding missing angles in a geometrical shape

Example

l and m are parallel lines.

Find the value of x and the value of y, in the diagram.

Solution

$x° = 25°$ (Vertically opposite angles)

Enter the alternate angle of $25°$, as shown in blue on the diagram:

$y° + 25° = 180°$ (Straight line)

$\quad y° = 180° - 25°$ (Subtract $25°$ from both sides)

$\quad y° = 155°$

Example

[AB] is a diameter of a circle.

C is a point on the circle and $|\angle ABC| = 75°$.

(i) Write down $|\angle ACB|$ and give a reason for your answer.

(ii) Calculate $|\angle BAC|$.

(iii) D is another point on the circle and $|\angle ABD| = 55°$. Find $|\angle DAC|$.

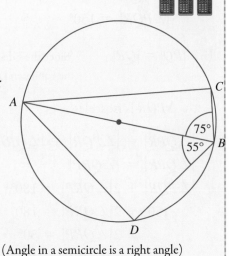

Solution

(i) $|\angle ACB| = 90°$ (Angle in a semicircle is a right angle)

(ii) $|\angle BAC| + 90° + 75° = 180°$ (Angles in a triangle sum to 180°)

        $|\angle BAC| + 165° = 180°$

            $|\angle BAC| = 180° - 165°$ (Subtract 165° from both sides)

            $|\angle BAC| = 15°$

(iii) $|\angle DAC| + |\angle DBC| = 180°$ (Opposite angle of a cyclic quadrilateral sum to 180°)

     $|\angle DAC| + (55° + 75°) = 180°$

        $|\angle DAC| + 130° = 180°$

           $|\angle DAC| = 180° - 130°$

           $|\angle DAC| = 50°$

Example

The diagram shows a square on top of an equilateral triangle QRS.

The point P is joined to R.

(i) Find $|\angle PQR|$.

(ii) Find $|\angle QRP|$.

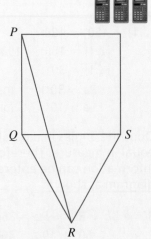

Solution

(i) $|\angle PQS| = 90°$ (One angle of a square)

   $|\angle SQR| = 60°$ (One angle of an equilateral triangle)

   $|\angle PQR| = |\angle PQS| + |\angle SQR|$

$$|\angle PQR| = 90° + 60°$$
$$|\angle PQR| = 150°$$

(ii) $|PQ| = |QR|$ (Since the sides of the square equal the sides of the equilateral triangle)

$\therefore \triangle PQR$ is isosceles

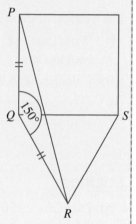

$$|\angle QPR| + |\angle PQR| + |\angle QRP| = 180°$$
$$|\angle QPR| = |\angle QRP| \quad \text{(Since } \triangle PQR \text{ is isosceles)}$$
$$|\angle PQR| + 2|\angle QRP| = 180°$$
$$\therefore \quad 150° + 2|\angle QRP| = 180°$$
$$2|\angle QRP| = 30°$$
$$|\angle QRP| = 15°$$

exam Q

The diagram shows a parallelogram and one exterior angle. Find the value of *a* and the value of *b*.

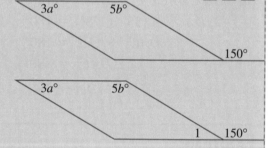

Solution

Construction:
Label the angle 1, as in the diagram.

Proof:
$$|\angle 1| + 150° = 180° \quad \text{(Straight angle)}$$
$$|\angle 1| = 180° - 150°$$
$$|\angle 1| = 30°$$
$$3a = 30° \quad \text{(Opposite angles of a parallelogram)}$$
$$\therefore \ a = 10° \quad \text{(Divide both sides by 3)}$$

Opposite angles in a parallelogram are equal in measure. Therefore, the information can be entered into the diagram as shown:

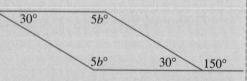

$$30° + 5b + 30° + 5b = 360° \quad \text{(Angles in a parallelogram sum to 360°)}$$
$$60° + 10b = 360°$$
$$10b = 300° \quad \text{(Subtract 60° from both sides)}$$
$$b = 30° \quad \text{(Divide both sides by 10°)}$$

Example

In the diagram, $|PQ| = |PR|$.

Find the value of:

(i) x (ii) y (iii) z

In each case give a reason for your answer.

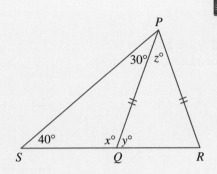

Solution

(i) In ΔSQP:

$$40° + 30° + x° = 180° \quad \text{(three angles of a triangle sum to 180°)}$$
$$70° + x° = 180°$$
$$x° = 110°$$

(ii) In ΔSQP:

$$40° + 30° = y° \qquad \text{(exterior angle equals sum}$$
$$70° = y° \qquad\qquad \text{of opposite interior angles)}$$

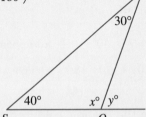

Alternatively:

$$x° + y° = 180° \qquad \text{(straight angle)}$$
$$110° + y° = 180°$$
$$y° = 70°$$

(iii) Enter the values for x and y into the diagram:

ΔPQR is isosceles.

$$\therefore |\angle PQR| = |\angle PRQ|$$
$$70° = |\angle PRQ|$$

In ΔPQR:

$$70° + 70° + z° = 180° \quad \text{(three angles of a triangle sum to 180°)}$$
$$140° + z° = 180°$$
$$z° = 40°$$

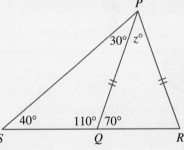

If l_1, l_2 and l_3 are parallel lines, find the measure of the angles α, β and γ.

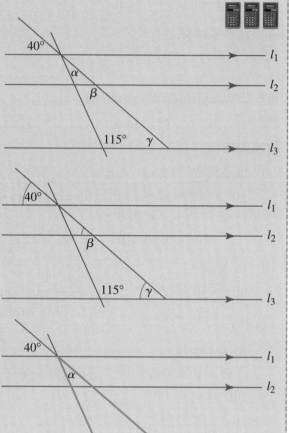

Solution

From the diagram, the three angles marked in red are corresponding angles, so they are all equal to each other.

$\therefore \gamma = 40°$　　　(corresponding angles)

$40° + \beta = 180°$　(straight angle)

　$\therefore \beta = 140°$

In the triangle coloured red,

the three angles of a triangle sum to 180°:

$\alpha + 40° + 115° = 180°$
$\alpha + 155° = 180°$
　$\therefore \alpha = 25°$

If $l_1 \| l_2$, find the measure of the angles α, β and γ in the diagram.

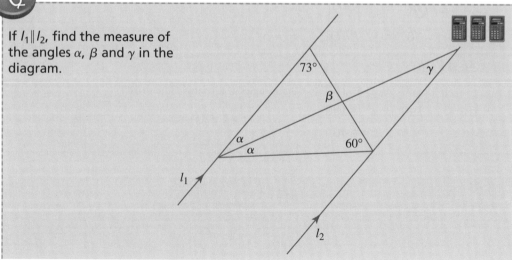

Solution

In the centre triangle:

$\alpha + \alpha + 73° + 60° = 180°$ (angles in a triangle sum to 180°)

$2\alpha + 133° = 180°$

$2\alpha = 47°$

$\alpha = 23·5°$

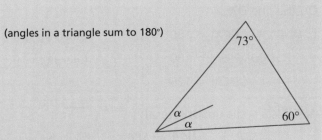

In the top triangle:

$23·5° + 73° + \beta = 180°$ (angles in a triangle sum to 180°)

$96·5° + \beta = 180°$

$\beta = 83·5°$

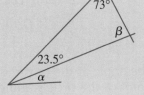

Since $l_1 \parallel l_2$:

$\alpha = \gamma$ (alternate angles)

$\therefore 23·5° = \gamma$

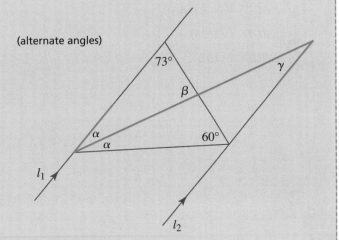

In the diagram, $|\angle XCB| = 54°$ and O is the centre of the circle.

Calculate $|\angle BOD|$, where $\angle BOD$ is obtuse.

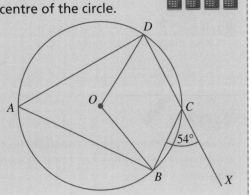

Solution

On the line *DX*:

$$|\angle DCB| + |\angle BCX| = 180° \qquad \text{(straight angle)}$$
$$|\angle DCB| + 54° = 180° \qquad \text{(straight angle)}$$
$$|\angle DCB| = 126°$$

ABCD is a cyclic quadrilateral:

$$\therefore |\angle DAB| + |\angle DCB| = 180° \qquad \text{(opposite angles in a cyclic quadrilateral sum to 180°)}$$
$$|\angle DAB| + 126° = 180°$$
$$|\angle DAB| = 54°$$

The angle at the centre of a circle standing on a given arc is twice the angle at any point of the circle standing on the same arc.

$$\therefore |\angle BOD| = 2|\angle DAB|$$
$$|\angle BOD| = 2(54)$$
$$|\angle BOD| = 108°$$

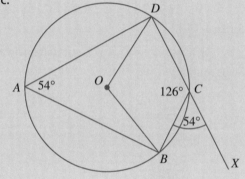

exam
Q

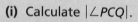

R is a point on a circle, with centre *C* and $|\angle CPQ| = 40°$.

(i) Calculate $|\angle PCQ|$.

(ii) Calculate $|\angle PRQ|$.

(iii) If $|\angle PCR| = 200°$, as shown in the diagram, calculate $|\angle CRP|$.

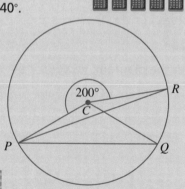

exam
focus

Always read the question carefully to pick out any information which has not been drawn on the diagram.

Solution

(i) $\triangle CPQ$ is isosceles since $[CP]$ and $[CQ]$ are both radii of the circle.

$|\angle CPQ| = 40°$ (given)

$\therefore |\angle CQP| = 40°$

$40 + |\angle PCQ| + 40 = 180$

$\therefore |\angle PCQ| = 100°$

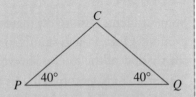

(ii) $\angle PCQ$ and $\angle PRQ$ are standing on the same arc. However, $\angle PCQ$ is at the centre of the circle and $\angle PRQ$ is at the circle.

Theorem: The angle at the centre of a circle standing on a given arc is twice the angle at any point of the circle standing on the same arc.

$\therefore |\angle PCQ| = 2|\angle PRQ|$

$100° = 2|\angle PRQ|$

$50° = |\angle PRQ|$

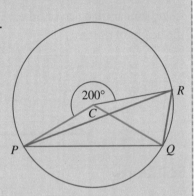

(iii) The angle at the centre of the circle is 360°:

$|\angle PCR| = 360 - 200$

$\therefore |\angle PCR| = 160°$

$|CP| = |CR|$ (both radii)

$\therefore \triangle CPR$ is isosceles

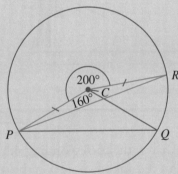

In $\triangle CPR$, the three angles of the triangle sum to 180°:

$|\angle PCR| + |\angle CPR| + |\angle CRP| = 180°$

$|\angle CPR| = |\angle CRP|$ (since $\triangle CPR$ is isosceles)

$160 + 2|\angle CRP| = 180°$

$2|\angle CRP| = 20°$

$|\angle CRP| = 10°$

Finding missing sides or lengths in a geometrical shape

Example

Some students wish to estimate the height of a tree standing on level ground. One of them stands so that the end of his shadow coincides with the end of the shadow of the tree, as shown in the diagram.

This student is 1·62 m tall. His friend then measures the distances shown in the diagram.

Using similar triangles, or otherwise, find the height of the tree.

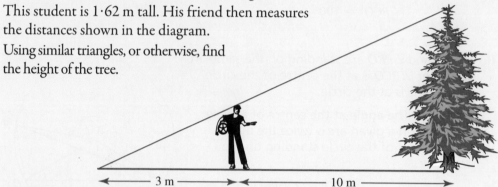

Solution

The diagram contains two similar triangles, since they have a common angle and they both contain a 90° angle. Redraw the similar triangles separately:

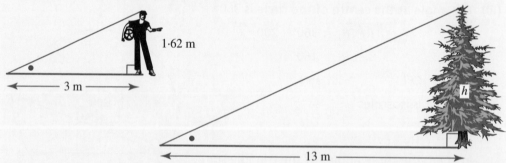

Analyse the corresponding sides:
Put the unknown side on the top of the left side of the fraction: $\dfrac{h}{1\cdot62} = \dfrac{13}{3}$

Large triangle	Small triangle
h	1·62
13	3

$$1\cdot62\left(\frac{h}{1\cdot62}\right) = 1\cdot62\left(\frac{13}{3}\right) \quad \text{(multiply both sides by 1·62)}$$

$$h = 1\cdot62\left(\frac{13}{3}\right)$$

$$h = 7\cdot02 \text{ m}$$

The two triangles shown are similar.

Find the value of *x*.

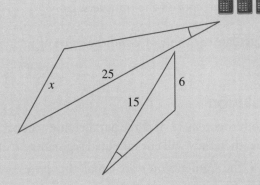

Solution

Redraw the triangles, so that they are facing the same way.

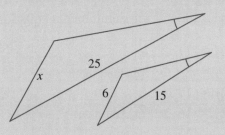

It is not necessary to redraw similar triangles. However it is good practice, as is can make it easier to identify the corresponding sides.

If there is not enough space to redraw the triangles on your exam paper, ask the exam superintendent for some extra paper.

Analyse the corresponding sides:
Put the unknown side on the top of the left side of the fraction: $\dfrac{x}{6} = \dfrac{25}{15}$

Large triangle	Small triangle
x	6
25	15

$$6\left(\frac{x}{6}\right) = 6\left(\frac{25}{15}\right) \quad \text{(multiply both sides by 6)}$$

$$x = \frac{150}{15}$$

$$x = 10$$

Example

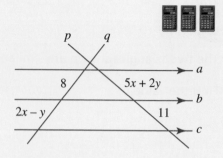

The lines a, b and c are parallel lines. They cut equal intercepts on the transversal, p.

Calculate the value of x and the value of y.

Solution

From theorem 11, if three parallel lines cut off equal segments on some transversal line, then they will cut off equal segments on any other transversal. Thus we can say:

- the segments on p are equal, therefore $5x + 2y = 11$
- the segments on q are equal, therefore $2x - y = 8$

Solve for x and y, using simultaneous equations:

$5x + 2y = 11$ ①
$\underline{2x - y = 8}$ ②   (multiply by 2)
$5x + 2y = 11$ ①
$\underline{4x - 2y = 16}$ ②   (add the rows)
$9x \quad\quad = 27$
$\quad x \quad\quad = 3$

Now solve for y:
$\quad 5x + 2y = 11$ ①
$\quad 5(3) + 2y = 11$ (substitute in value for x)
$\quad 15 + 2y = 11$
$\quad\quad\quad 2y = -4$
$\quad\quad\quad y = -2$

Notice the link to simultaneous equations in algebra, which is normally associated with paper 1.

Example

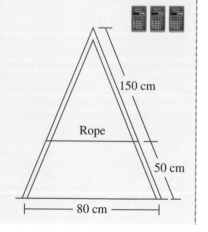

The rope on a pair of stepladders, as shown, stops the steps from opening too far.

Using similar triangles, find the length of the rope.

150 cm

Rope

50 cm

80 cm

Solution

Redraw the two triangles separately and fill in all known sides.

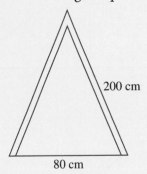

200 cm

80 cm

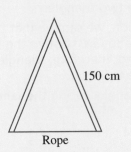

150 cm

Rope

Analyse the corresponding sides.

Large triangle	Small triangle
200	150
80	Rope

Put the unknown side on the top of the left side of the fraction.

$$\frac{\text{Rope}}{80} = \frac{150}{200}$$

$$80\left(\frac{\text{Rope}}{80}\right) = 80\left(\frac{150}{200}\right) \quad \text{(multiply both sides by 80)}$$

$$\text{Rope} = \frac{12{,}000}{200}$$

$$\text{Rope} = 60 \text{ cm}$$

exam
Q

In the diagram, $CD \perp AB$.

$|\angle CBD| = 35°$ and $|\angle CAD| = 55°$.

$|CD| = 7$, $|DB| = 10$ and $|AD| = x$.

(i) Show that the triangles CAD and CDB are similar.

(ii) Hence, find x.

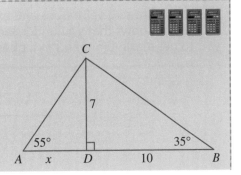

Solution

(i) Use the theorem 4: the three angles of a triangle sum to 180°. Fill the missing angles into the two triangles.

From observation, we can see that the triangles *CAD* and *CDB* contain the same angles and, therefore, triangles *CAD* and *CDB* are similar.

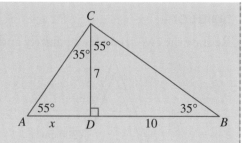

(ii) Redraw the triangles facing the same way:

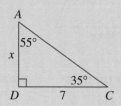

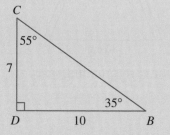

Analyse the corresponding sides.

Put the unknown side on the top of the left side of the fraction.

$$\frac{x}{7} = \frac{7}{10}$$

$$7\left(\frac{x}{7}\right) = 7\left(\frac{7}{10}\right) \quad \text{(multiply both sides by 7)}$$

$$x = 4{\cdot}9$$

Small triangle	Large triangle
x	7
7	10

Using geometry to prove statements

It is important to give reasons and explanations for statements made during a proof. This shows that you understand the steps you are taking and so will help you to get maximum marks in a question.

Prove that $x + y + z = 360°$.

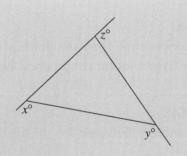

Solution

Construction:

Label the angles 1 and 2, as in the diagram.

Proof:

$$|\angle 1| = 180° - z \qquad \text{(straight angle)}$$
$$|\angle 2| = 180° - y \qquad \text{(straight angle)}$$
$$x = |\angle 1| + |\angle 2| \qquad \text{(exterior angle equals sum of interior opposite angles)}$$
$$\therefore \qquad x = 180° - z + 180° - y$$
$$x + y + z = 180° + 180°$$
$$\therefore x + y + z = 360°$$

C is the centre of the circle k. $[AB]$ and $[XY]$ are diameters of k.

(i) Name another line segment equal in length to $[AC]$. Give a reason for your answer.

(ii) Prove that $\triangle ACX$ and $\triangle BCY$ are congruent.

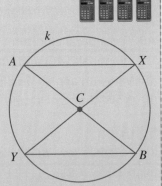

Solution

(i) $[CX]$, $[CY]$ or $[CB]$ are equal in length to the line segment $[AC]$.

All of these line segments are radii of the circle k.

(ii) Look at $\triangle ACX$ and $\triangle BCY$:

$$|CA| = |CB| \qquad \text{(both radii)}$$
$$|CX| = |CY| \qquad \text{(both radii)}$$
$$|\angle ACX| = |\angle BCY| \qquad \text{(vertically opposite angles)}$$
$$\therefore \triangle ACX \equiv \triangle BCY \qquad \text{(SAS rule)}$$

Congruent triangles

Two triangles are congruent if they are identical in size and shape.

You must know the four rules for congruency. We can say that two triangles are congruent if:

SAS	ASA
Two sides and the angle in between are the same in both.	Two angles and a side are the same in both.

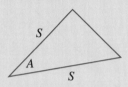

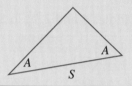

SSS	RHS
All three sides are the same in both.	Right angle, hypotenuse and another side are the same in both.

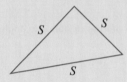

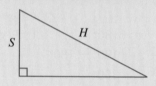

ABCD is a parallelogram.

The diagonals [AC] and [BD] intersect at the point O.

 (i) Name an angle equal in measure to ∠DAO.

(ii) Prove that ΔAOD and ΔBOC are congruent.

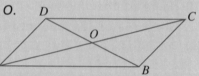

Solution

 (i) |∠DAO| = |∠BCO|, because they are alternate angles.

(ii) |AD| = |CB| (opposite sides of a parallelogram)

    |∠DAO| = |∠BCO| (alternate angles)

    |∠ADO| = |∠CBO| (alternate angles)

    Therefore, ΔAOD and ΔBOC are congruent (ASA).

exam Q

(i) Prove that [AE bisects ∠DAC.

(ii) Would the result in part (i) still apply
if |AB| and |AC| were not equal?

Give a reason for your answer.

key point

Arrows indicate that lines
are parallel.

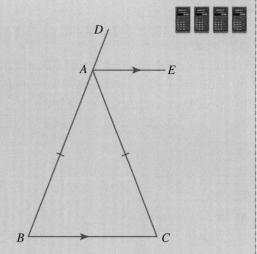

Solution

(i) To prove that [AE bisects ∠DAC,
we must show that |∠DAE| = |∠CAE|.

Label the angles 1, 2 and 3 and as in the diagram.

	∠2	=	∠4		(alternate angles)
	∠1	=	∠3		(corresponding angles)
	∠3	=	∠4		(isosceles triangle)

∴ |∠1| = |∠2|

∴ |∠DAE| = |∠CAE|

Thus, [AE bisects ∠DAC.

(ii) If |AB| and |AC| were not equal, the result
in (i) would not apply. Angle 3 would not be
equal to angle 4.

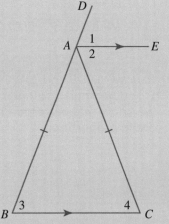

exam focus

In a recent exam, this question was very poorly answered.
Consequently (i) and (ii) **together** were awarded a total of 5 marks.

A, B, C and D are four points on a circle as shown.
[AD] bisects ∠BAC.

P is the point of intersection of AD and BC.

(i) Show that △ADB and △APC are similar.

(ii) Show that $|AC||BD| = |AD||PC|$

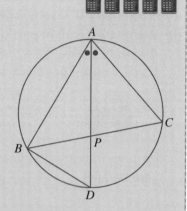

Solution

(i) In △ADB and △APC:

$|∠BAD| = |∠PAC|$ (since [AD] bisects ∠BAC)

$|∠ADB| = |∠ACP|$ (both angles standing on the same arc, AB)

∴ △ADB and △APC are similar.   (two pair of equal angles)

(ii) Redraw △ADB and △APC separately.
From the similar triangles theorem,
we know that corresponding sides
are in proportion:

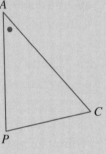

∴ $\dfrac{|AC|}{|AD|} = \dfrac{|PC|}{|BD|}$

$|AD||BD|\dfrac{|AC|}{|AD|} = |AD||BD|\dfrac{|PC|}{|BD|}$ (multiply both sides by $|AD|\,|BD|$)

∴ $|AC||BD| = |AD||PC|$

QR and *QP* are both tangents to circle *c* with centre *O*.

(i) If $|\angle PSR| = 57°$, find *x*.

(ii) Prove that $|QR| = |QP|$.

Solution

(i) Construct the radii *OR* and *OP*.

$|\angle ORQ| = 90°$ (*RQ* is a tangent)

$|\angle OPQ| = 90°$ (*PQ* is a tangent)

$|\angle ROP| = 114°$ ($|\angle ROP| = 2|\angle RSP|$, since angle at the centre is twice the angle at the circle standing on the same arc)

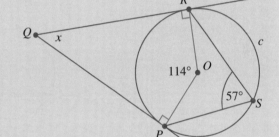

$|\angle ORQ| + |\angle OPQ| + |\angle PQR| + |\angle ROP| = 360°$ (4 angles of a quadrilateral)

$$90° + 90° + x + 114° = 360°$$

$$x = 66°$$

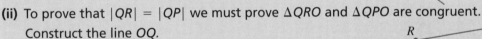

(ii) To prove that $|QR| = |QP|$ we must prove $\triangle QRO$ and $\triangle QPO$ are congruent.

Construct the line *OQ*.

$|OR| = |OP|$ (both radii)

$|OQ| = |OQ|$ (common line)

$|\angle ORQ| = |\angle OPQ|$ (both 90°)

$\therefore \triangle QRO \equiv \triangle QPO$ (RHS)

$\therefore \quad |QR| = |QP|$

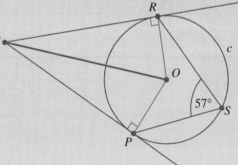

We could also have proven $|QR| = |QP|$ by showing the $\triangle PQR$ is isosceles.

l_1 and l_2 are lines. c_1 and c_2 are circles. A, B and C are points.
Draw a diagram to illustrate the following statement:
$l_1 \cap c_1 = \{A, B\}$, $l_1 \cap c_2 = \{B, C\}$ and $l_1 \cap l_2 = \{C\}$

Solution

- The line l_1 crosses through the circle c_1 at two points, A and B.
- The line l_1 crosses through the circle c_2 at two points, B and C.
- Since the point B is on the line l_1 and the two circles, c_1 and c_2, all three objects must meet at the point B.
- Since the point C is on the lines l_1 and l_2 and the circle c_2, all three objects must meet at the point C.

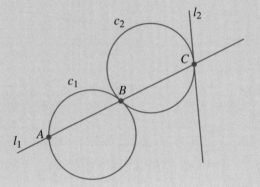

The above diagram is not a unique solution. There will be other similar diagrams which fulfil the given criteria.

3 Constructions

aims

- ☐ To be able to complete all 15 constructions
- ☐ To be able to use your knowledge of constructions to solve practical problems

On the Junior Certificate Higher Level course, you must be able to perform 15 constructions.

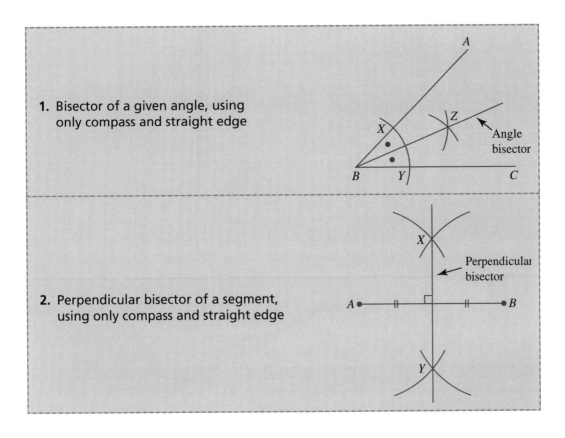

1. Bisector of a given angle, using only compass and straight edge

2. Perpendicular bisector of a segment, using only compass and straight edge

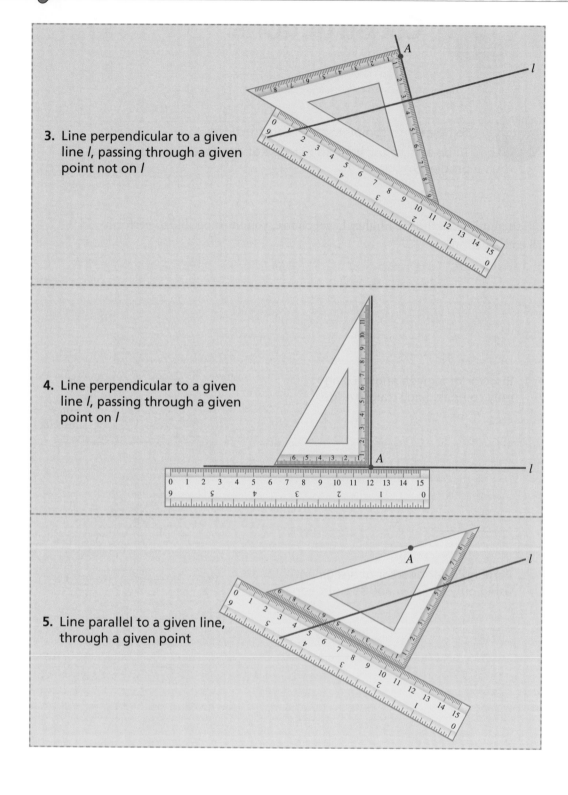

3. Line perpendicular to a given line *l*, passing through a given point not on *l*

4. Line perpendicular to a given line *l*, passing through a given point on *l*

5. Line parallel to a given line, through a given point

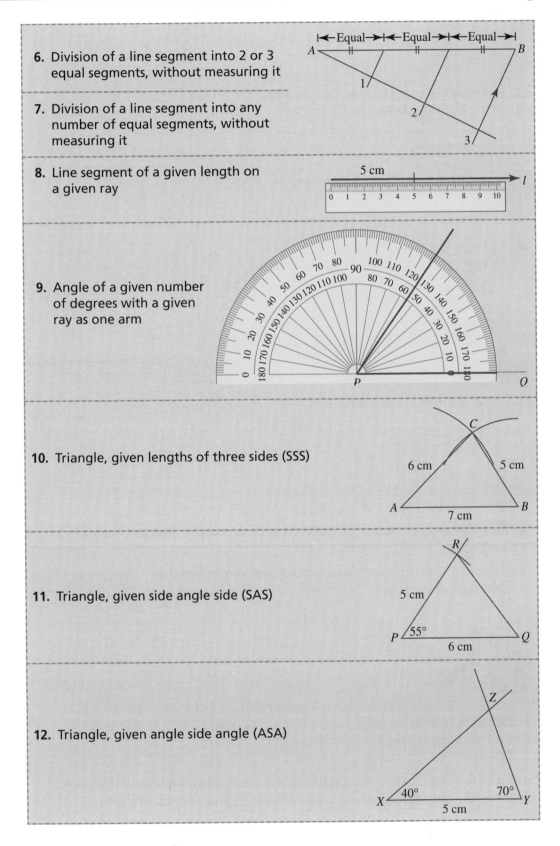

6. Division of a line segment into 2 or 3 equal segments, without measuring it

7. Division of a line segment into any number of equal segments, without measuring it

8. Line segment of a given length on a given ray

9. Angle of a given number of degrees with a given ray as one arm

10. Triangle, given lengths of three sides (SSS)

11. Triangle, given side angle side (SAS)

12. Triangle, given angle side angle (ASA)

13. **Right-angled triangle, given the length of the hypotenuse and one other side**

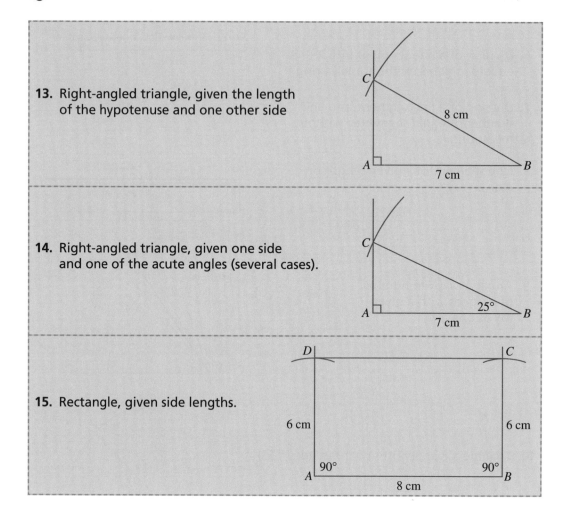

14. **Right-angled triangle, given one side and one of the acute angles (several cases).**

15. **Rectangle, given side lengths.**

- The steps required for completing each of these constructions are detailed in your text book.
- Computer simulations of these constructions can be found at www.mathopenref.com.

exam focus

To draw an accurate construction, you need a sharp pencil, an eraser, a compass, a ruler, a set square and a protractor. Make sure you have a full mathematical set with you in your exam.

Note: The diagrams for the constructions given as solutions throughout this chapter may not be the exact measurement stated. They are representations of the required solution.

Selection of examples and exam questions involving constructions

Example

(i) Construct a line segment [AB], 5 cm in length.

(ii) Hence construct the perpendicular bisector of [AB].

Solution

(i) Construct the line segment 5 cm in length:

A ———————————————— B

(ii) To construct the perpendicular bisector:

Step 1: Set the compass to a radius of about three-quarters of the length of the line segment [AB].

(Any radius above half the length of the line segment will do.)

A •———————————————— B

Place the compass point on A and draw arcs above and below the line segment.

Step 2: Keep the same radius as in step 1.

Place the compass point on B and draw arcs above and below the line segment to intersect the other arcs.

Where the arcs intersect, label the points X and Y.

Step 3: Draw the line through X and Y.

The line XY is the perpendicular bisector of the line segment [AB].

X

Perpendicular bisector

A ——+——▢——+—— B

key point

Any point on the perpendicular bisector of a line segment [AB] is equidistant (the same distance) from the points A and B. The perpendicular bisector of the line segment [AB] is always at right angles to the line segment.

Y

It is important to show **all** construction lines or marks you make at any stage during the construction. Erasing any of these may result in marks being lost in an exam.

exam Q

(i) Construct an angle ABC such that $|\angle ABC| = 70°$.

(ii) Hence, bisect the angle ABC using only a compass and a straight edge.

Solution

(i) Draw the line segment $[BC]$

Place the centre of the protractor at the point B. Starting from the 0° mark at C, mark the position of 70°.

This is the position for the line segment $[BA]$.

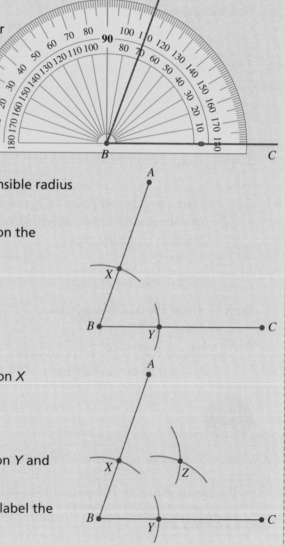

(ii) To bisect the angle ABC:

Step 1: Set your compass to a sensible radius (not too large).

Place the compass point on the vertex, B.

Draw two arcs to intersect the arms at X and Y.

Step 2: Place the compass point on X and draw an arc.

Keep the same radius.

Place the compass point on Y and draw an arc.

Where the arcs intersect, label the point Z.

Step 3: Draw a line from *B* through the point *Z*.

The line *BZ* is the bisector of the angle *ABC*.

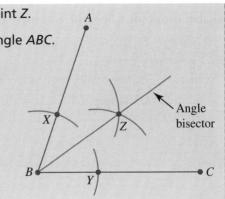

key point

Any point on the bisector of an angle is equidistant (the same distance) from the arms of the angle.

The bisector of an acute or obtuse angle also bisects its related reflex angle.

Example

Construct the triangle *ABC* such that $|AB| = 7$ cm, $|AC| = 6$ cm and $|BC| = 5$ cm.

Solution

Step 1: Draw a rough sketch of the triangle

Step 2: Using a ruler, draw a horizontal line segment 7 cm in length.

Label the end points *A* and *B*.

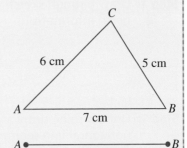

Step 3: Set your compass to a radius of 6 cm.

Place the compass point on the point *A*.
Draw an arc above the line segment.

Set your compass to a radius of 5 cm.
Place the compass point on the point *B*.
Draw an arc above the line segment to meet the other arc.

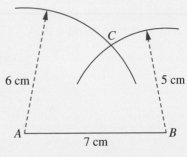

Note: Measurements shown here are not exact. They are a representation of the correct solution.

Label the point where the arcs meet C.

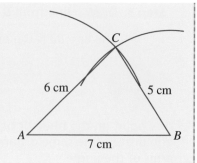

Step 4: Using your ruler, join A to C and B to C.
The triangle ABC is now drawn as required.

exam
Q

Construct a triangle ABC such that $|\angle BAC| = 45°$, $|\angle ABC| = 58°$ and $|AB| = 7$ cm.

Solution

Step 1: Draw a rough sketch with the
given information.

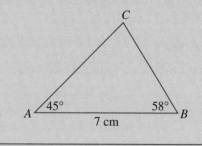

Step 2: Using a ruler, draw a
horizontal line segment
7 cm in length.
Label the end points A and B.

Step 3: Place your protractor on the point A.
Draw an angle of 45°.

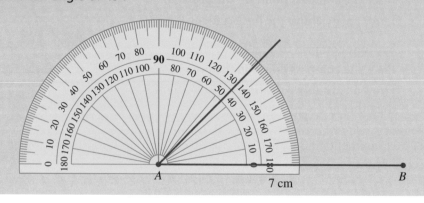

Step 4: Place your protractor on the point *B*.

Draw an angle of 58°.

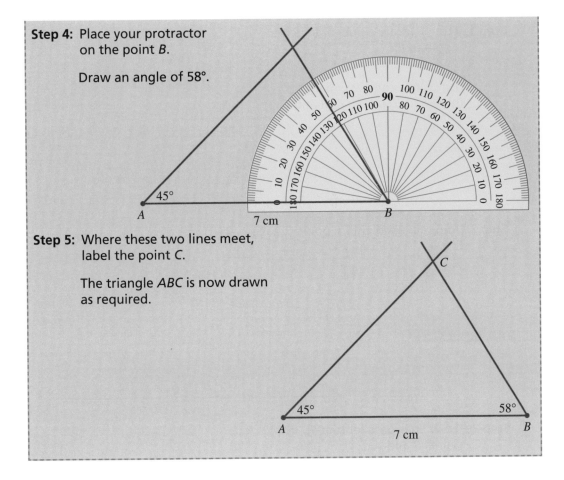

Step 5: Where these two lines meet, label the point *C*.

The triangle *ABC* is now drawn as required.

If *Q* and *R* are two points between *P* and *S* on a line segment [*PS*], such that |*PQ*| = |*QR*| = |*RS*|:

(i) Draw the line segment [*PS*], 8 cm long.

(ii) Show how to construct accurately the points *Q* and *R*.

Solution

(i) Construct a line segment 8 cm in length and label the end points *P* and *S*:

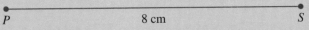

P   8 cm   *S*

(ii) Since |*PQ*| = |*QR*| = |*RS*|. The points *Q* and *R* divide the line segment [*PS*] into three equal parts.

To divide a line segment into three equal parts:

Step 1: From *P*, draw a line at an acute angle to *PS*.

Using your compass, mark off three equal spaces, *A*, *B* and *C*.

Step 2: Join the last division, point *C*, to *S*.

Step 3: Draw lines parallel to [*CS*], from points *B* and *A*.

The line segment is now divided into three equal parts.

Label the points *Q* and *R*.

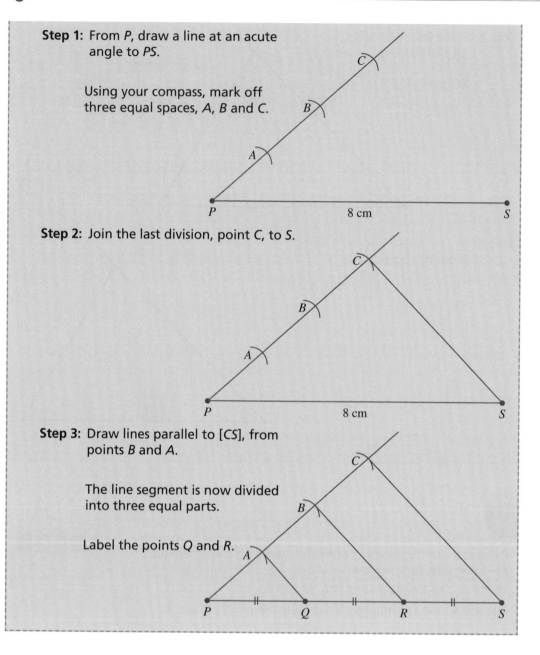

The diagram shows a rectangular garden, 24 m by 18 m. A tree is to be planted in the garden.

The tree must be 12 m from *P* and the tree must be an equal distance from *SR* and *RQ*.

Using only a compass and straight edge, construct the position of the tree.

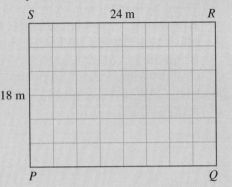

Solution

Step 1: Put the compass point on *P* and open it to half the width of the 24 m line. This gives a radius of 12 m.

Draw an arc, centred at the point *P*, with a radius of 12 m.

This arc represents all points which are a distance of 12 m from *P*.

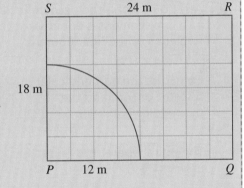

Step 2: A line which is equal distance from both *SR* and *RQ* is on the bisector of the angle $\angle SRQ$.

Construct the bisector of the angle $\angle SRQ$.
The point where the 12 m arc and the angle bisector intersect is the position for the tree.

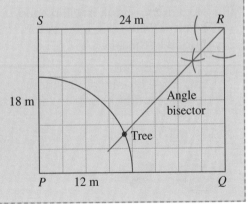

Any point on the bisector of an angle is equidistant from the arms of the angle.

(i) The diagram shows an island, with a lake. There is treasure buried at a point *T*, where *T* is equidistant from *A* and *B* and is also equidistant from *C* and *D*.

Using only a compass and straight edge, locate the point *T*.

(ii) Do you think it will be easy to retrieve the treasure?

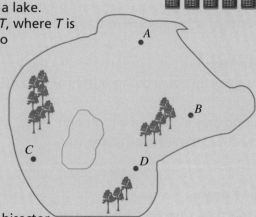

Solution

(i) Any point along the perpendicular bisector of a line segment is equidistant from the two ends of the line segment.

Construct the perpendicular bisector of [*AB*] and the perpendicular bisector of [*CD*].

The point where these bisectors intersect is *T*.

(ii) No, I do not think it will be easy to retrieve the treasure, as it is buried in the lake.

   or

Yes, it will be easy as we know its exact location and we can use diving equipment.

In the exam, when you are asked for your opinion you must be aware that there may be more than one valid answer as in part (ii) above. Whatever opinion you give, it is important that you have reasons to back it up.

4 Transformation Geometry

aims

☐ To learn how to find the image of objects under:
  ○ translation
  ○ axial symmetry
  ○ central symmetry.
☐ To learn how to locate axes of symmetry in simple shapes
☐ To be able to recognise images of points and objects under:
  ○ translation
  ○ axial symmetry
  ○ central symmetry.

Transformations

The word '**transformation**' means change. The movement of a point or a shape from one position to another is called a **transformation**. In other words, a transformation changes the position of a shape.

Object and image

The original position of a shape is called the **object**. The new position of the shape is called the **image**. The image is where the object moves to. We say that the object **maps onto** the image.

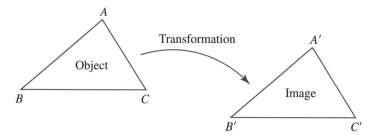

- Often the images of points are indicated by primes. A' is pronounced 'A prime'.
- A and A' are called **corresponding** points because the point A' is the image of the point A.
- A figure has **critical** points that define its shape, usually its vertices (corners).
- When constructing an image, we usually only find the image of the critical points.
- In the triangle above, the critical points are A, B and C and their images are A', B' and C', respectively. Then we join the image points to construct the image of the object.

On our course, we will learn about three types of transformations:

1. Translation,   **2.** Axial symmetry   **3.** Central symmetry

> Each of these transformations changes the position of a shape but not its size or shape.

Translation

Under a translation, every point in the shape is moved the same distance in the same direction. It is often called a **slide**, since the shape appears to slide from one position to another. The shape does not turn or flip over. The object and its image are congruent (identical).

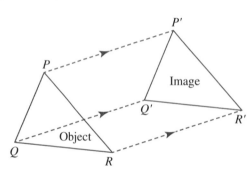

To describe a translation, we need to give its direction and say by how much it has moved. A translation is often denoted by an arrow above two letters, for example $\overrightarrow{AB}$ or $\overrightarrow{AA'}$. The translation shown on the left could be described as $P \rightarrow P'$, written as $\overrightarrow{PP'}$.

The translation could also be written as $\overrightarrow{QQ'}$ or $\overrightarrow{RR'}$. Under a translation, lengths and angles are preserved.

key point

A translation can be described using a **column vector**. A column vector is written similar to coordinates, with the left or right (horizontal) displacement on top and the up or down (vertical) displacement on the bottom.

$\begin{pmatrix} 4 \\ -3 \end{pmatrix}$ is a translation of 4 units to the right and 3 units down.

$\begin{pmatrix} -2 \\ 5 \end{pmatrix}$ is a translation of 2 units to the left and 5 units up.

$\begin{pmatrix} -1 \\ -4 \end{pmatrix}$ is a translation of 1 unit to the left and 4 units down.

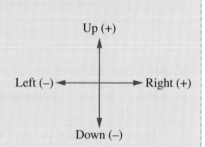

Example

The diagram shows triangle A.

(i) Construct the image of A under the translation 4 units right and 2 units up. Label this image B.

(ii) Construct the image of B under the translation 3 units right and 5 units down. Label this image C.

(iii) Describe the single translation that maps A onto C.

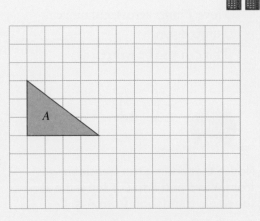

Solution

(i) Chose a point on the triangle A and move it 4 units to the right and 2 units up.

This can also be written as:

$$\begin{pmatrix} 4 \\ 2 \end{pmatrix}$$

Draw the triangle B at this new position.

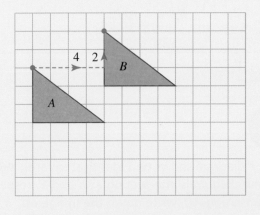

(ii) Chose a point on the triangle B and move it 3 units to the right and 5 units down.

This can also be written as:

$$\begin{pmatrix} 3 \\ -5 \end{pmatrix}$$

Draw the triangle C at this new position.

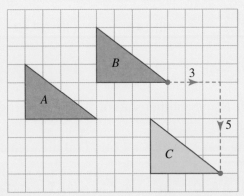

(iii) To move A to C:

Move 7 units across and move 3 units down.

This can also be written as:

key point

$$\binom{7}{-3}$$

Notice that adding the translations from A to B and B to C is the same as the single translation from A to C.

$A \rightarrow B + B \rightarrow C = A \rightarrow C$

$$\binom{4}{2} + \binom{3}{-5} = \binom{7}{-3}$$

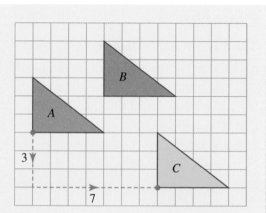

exam Q

The diagram shows two identical squares, *ABCD* and *DCEF*, with their diagonals intersecting at *X* and *Y*, respectively. Under the translation $\overrightarrow{AD}$, write down the image of:

(i) *C* (ii) [*AB*] (iii) △*AXD*

(iv) [*BX*] (v) [*XD*] (vi) ∠*XAD*

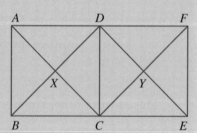

(vii) Name another square. Justify your choice.

If the area of △*ABX* is 4 cm², find the area of:

(viii) △*BAD* (ix) △*ACF* (x) The rectangle *ABEF*

Solution

The translation $\overrightarrow{AD}$ means to move to the right by the distance from point A to point D:

(i) $C \rightarrow E$

(ii) $[AB] \rightarrow [DC]$

(iii) $\triangle AXD \rightarrow \triangle DYF$

(iv) $[BX] \rightarrow [CY]$

(v) $[XD] \rightarrow [YF]$

(vi) $\angle XAD \rightarrow \angle YDF$

key point

It is good practice, but not necessary, to keep the order of the images of points asked in the question.

(vii) $DXCY$ is a square.

Reason: The diagonals of the squares $ABCD$ and $DCEF$ meet at right angles and bisect each other. This means the sides of $DXCY$ are equal in length and meet at right angles, and therefore $DXCY$ is a square.

(viii) $\triangle BAD = 2(\triangle ABX)$

$= 2(4)$

$= 8 \text{ cm}^2$

(ix) $\triangle ACF = 2(\triangle BAD)$

$= 2(8)$

$= 16 \text{ cm}^2$

(x) Rectangle $ABEF = 8(\triangle ABX)$

$= 8(4)$

$= 32 \text{ cm}^2$

Axial symmetry

Axial symmetry is a reflection in a line. It involves reflecting points perpendicularly through a line.

An object reflected in a mirror creates an image. A reflection in a line, known as an axial symmetry, produces an image that looks like a reflection in a mirror (sometimes called a mirror image). The line is called the **axis of reflection** or **line of reflection** or **mirror line**. The object and the image are symmetrical about the mirror line. In other words, any point and its image are the same perpendicular distance from the axis of symmetry. The object and the image are congruent. However, under a reflection in a line, a figure flips over.

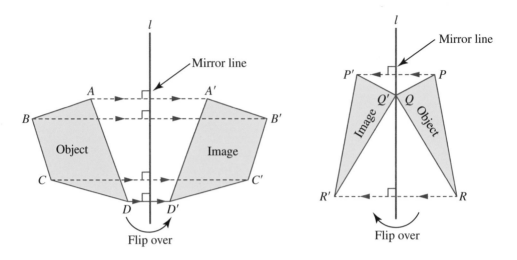

Axis of symmetry

A shape has an **axis of symmetry** or a **line of symmetry** when one half of the shape fits exactly over the other half when the shape is folded along that line. Shapes which are evenly balanced are said to be **symmetrical**. Some shapes have no axis of symmetry, some have only one axis of symmetry and others have more than one axis of symmetry.

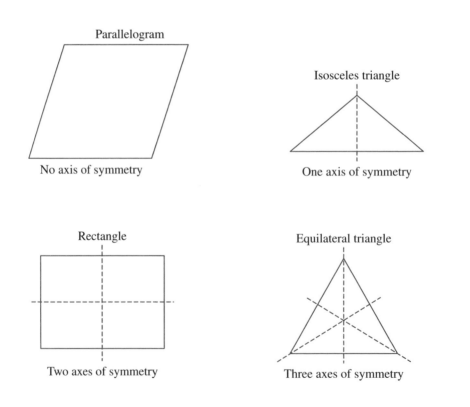

Example

Draw all axes of symmetry on the following shapes:

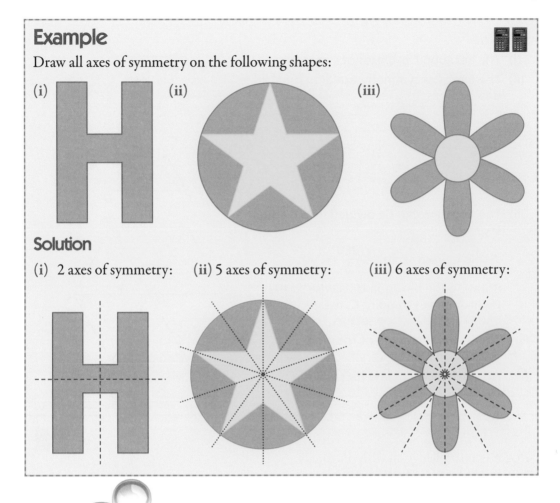

(i)   (ii)   (iii)

Solution

(i) 2 axes of symmetry: (ii) 5 axes of symmetry: (iii) 6 axes of symmetry:

exam focus

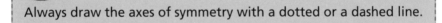

Always draw the axes of symmetry with a dotted or a dashed line.

exam Q

The diagram shows a regular hexagon (a regular hexagon has six equal sides and six equal angles).

(i) How many axes of symmetry has the hexagon?

(ii) Draw in the axes of symmetry.

(iii) [AD] and [CF] intersect at point O. What is the measure of the angle of the clockwise rotation, about O, which maps A onto C?

(iv) Describe one transformation which maps [AF] to [CD].

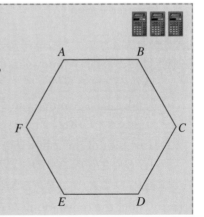

Solution

(i) The hexagon has 6 axes of symmetry.

(ii) The 6 axes of symmetry are drawn as red dashed lines:

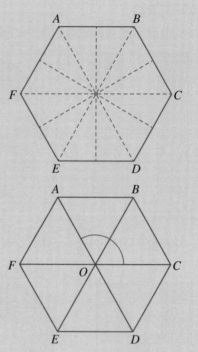

(iii) The hegagon can be divided into 6 equal segments.

$$\text{Angle in each sector} = \frac{360}{6} = 60°$$

Rotating the hexagon clockwise so that point A moves to point C, means it has been rotated by two sectors.

Therefore, the angle of rotation
= 2(60°) = 120°.

(iv) Axial symmetry in line [BE] will map [AF] to [CD].

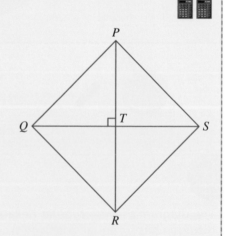

Example

$PQRS$ is a parallelogram with diagonals intersecting at T, and $PR \perp QS$.

(i) Find the image of $\triangle QRT$ under axial symmetry in QS.

(ii) What is the image of $PQRS$ under axial symmetry in PR?

(iii) Name four isosceles triangles.

(iv) Find the image of $[PQ]$ under the translation $\overrightarrow{QR}$.

Solution

(i) Under axial symmetry in QS:
$\triangle QRT \rightarrow \triangle QPT$

(ii) Under axial symmetry in PR:
$PQRS \rightarrow PSRQ$

(iii) Any four of the following:
$\triangle PQS, \triangle RQS, \triangle QRP, \triangle SRP,$
$\triangle PTQ, \triangle PTS, \triangle RTQ, \triangle RTS$

(iv) Under the translation $\overrightarrow{QR}$: $[PQ] \rightarrow [SR]$

key point

If a point is on the axis of symmetry (mirror line), its image is the same point.

key point

For the image of a point under:
- Axial symmetry in the *x*-axis: change the sign of *y*-coordinate
- Axial symmetry in the *y*-axis: change the sign of *x*-coordinate.

exam Q

(i) Write down the coordinates of the point A.

(ii) Find the point B, the image of the point A, under axial symmetry in the y-axis.

(iii) Find the point C, the image of the point (1, 3), under axial symmetry in the x-axis.

(iv) Find the equation of the line segment [BC], in the form $y = mx + c$.

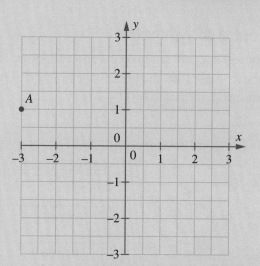

Solution

(i) $A = (-3, 1)$

(ii) Under axial symmetry in the y-axis, the sign of the x-coordinate changes. Therefore, $B = (3, 1)$.

(iii) Under axial symmetry in the x-axis, the sign of the y-coordinate changes. Therefore, $C = (1, -3)$.

(iv) To find the equation, we need the slope of the line: $B = (3, 1)$ $C = (1, -3)$

$$m = \frac{y_2 - y_1}{x_2 - x_1}$$

$$= \frac{-3 - 1}{1 - 3}$$

$$= \frac{-4}{-2}$$

$$m = 2$$

$y - y_1 = m(x - x_1)$

$y - 1 = 2(x - 3)$

$y - 1 = 2x - 6$

$y = 2x - 6 + 1$

$y = 2x - 5$

$[y] = 2x - 5$ is the equation of [BC]

exam focus

Notice the link to coordinate geometry in this question.

Central symmetry

An object reflected in a point creates an image. Under a central symmetry, any point and its image are equidistant from the centre of symmetry. The object and the image are congruent. However, under a central symmetry, a shape is turned over. Central symmetry is exactly the same as a rotation of 180° about the centre of symmetry.

> Central symmetry is a reflection in a point. The point is called the **centre of symmetry**.
>
> It involves reflecting points through the centre of symmetry to the same distance on the other side.

Centre of symmetry

Some shapes are symmetrical about a point. The point is called the **centre of symmetry** (sometimes called the point of symmetry). The following shapes have a centre of symmetry, indicated by O.

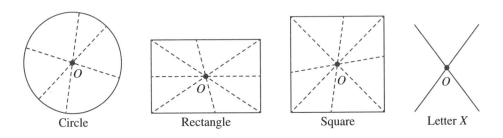

Circle   Rectangle   Square   Letter X

Example

Locate the centre of symmetry of the following shapes:

(i)   (ii)

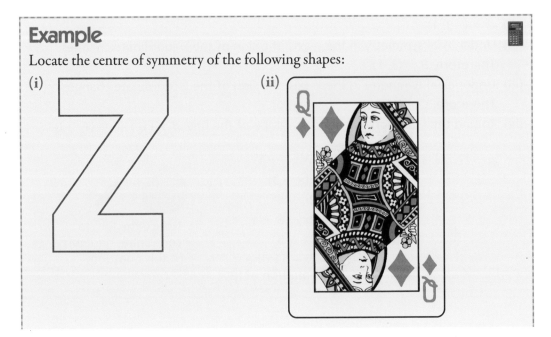

Solution

To locate the centre of symmetry for each shape:

1. Select a point on the shape and draw a line to the corresponding point on the opposite side of the shape.
2. Repeat this for many points on the shape.
3. The point where all of these lines intersect is the centre of symmetry of the shape.

(i)

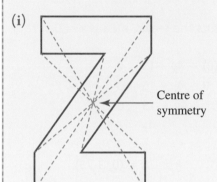

Centre of symmetry

(ii)

Centre of symmetry

Example

Construct the image of the figure under a central symmetry in the point O.

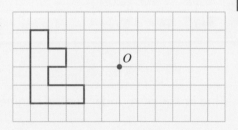

Solution

Draw a straight line from each corner (vertex) of the object to O and continue the same distance on the other side of O.

Join the points to construct the new shape.

The resulting shape is the image of the object under a central symmetry in O.

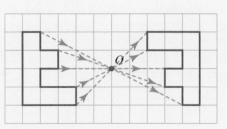

The line $3x - 4y + 15 = 0$ cuts the x-axis at A and the y-axis at B.

(i) Find the coordinates of A and the coordinates of B.

(ii) Plot the points A and B on the coordinated plane.

(iii) Find the coordinates of the image of A under central symmetry in the point B.

Solution

(i) Cuts the x-axis, means $y = 0$:

$$3x - 4(0) + 15 = 0$$
$$3x - 0 + 15 = 0$$
$$3x + 15 = 0$$
$$3x = -15$$
$$x = -5$$
$$A = (-5, 0)$$

Cuts the y-axis, means $x = 0$:

$$3(0) - 4y + 15 = 0$$
$$0 - 4y + 15 = 0$$
$$-4y + 15 = 0$$
$$-4y = -15$$
$$y = 3 \cdot 75$$
$$B = (0, 3 \cdot 75)$$

(ii)

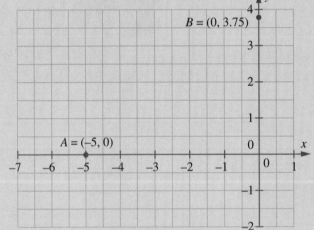

(iii) Find image of A under central symmetry in B:

$$\begin{array}{ccccc}
& +5, +3{\cdot}75 & & +5, +3{\cdot}75 & \\
A(-5, 0) & \rightarrow & B(0, 3{\cdot}75) & \rightarrow & C(5, 7{\cdot}5)
\end{array}$$

Notice the link to coordinate geometry here.

Each of the four diagrams *A*, *B*, *C* and *D* shows the object in Figure 1 and its image under a transformation.

For each of *A*, *B*, *C* and *D*, state one transformation (translation, axial symmetry or central symmetry) that will map the object onto that image.

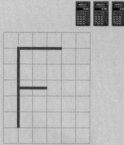

Figure 1

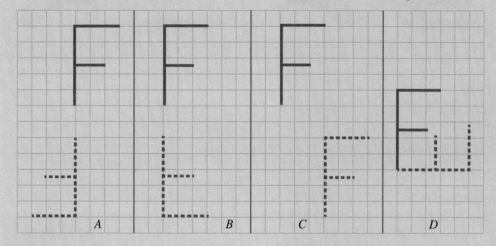

Solution

Image *A* is formed by central symmetry through a point (green dot).

Image *B* is formed by axial symmetry through a horizontal line (green line).

Image *C* is formed by translation: 3 units to the right and 7 units downwards.

Image *D* is formed by axial symmetry in a diagonal line (green line).

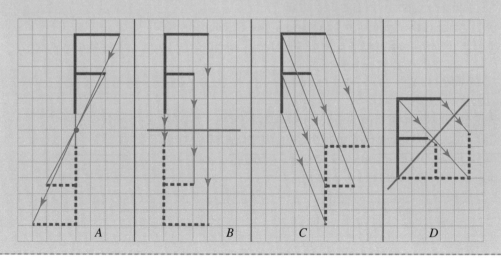

Each of the three figures labelled *A*, *B* and *C* shown below is the image of the object under a transformation. For each of *A*, *B* and *C*, state whether the transformation is a translation, an axial symmetry in the *x*-axis, an axial symmetry in the *y*-axis or a central symmetry.

Object   *A*   *B*   *C*

Solution

Image *A* is formed by central symmetry.

Image *B* is formed by axial symmetry in the *y*-axis.

Image *C* is formed by axial symmetry in the *x*-axis.

ABCD is a rectangle. *ABDX* and *BYCD* are parallelograms.

  (i) Name three line segments equal in length to [*DC*].

  (ii) What is the image of △*BCY* under central symmetry in *Z*?

  (iii) What is the image of △*AXD* under axial symmetry in the line *AD*?

  (iv) What is the image of [*AX*] under the translation $\vec{BY}$?

  (v) If the area of △*ADZ* = △*AZB* = 5 cm², what is the area of the figure *AXCY*?

Solution

  (i) [*AB*], [*XD*] and [*BY*]

  (ii) Under central symmetry in point *Z*: △*BCY* → △*DAX*

  (iii) Under axial symmetry in the line *AD*: △*AXD* → △*ACD*

  (iv) Under the translation $\vec{BY}$: [*AX*] → [*BD*]

  (v) The figure *AXCY* = 8(△*ADZ*)

$$= 8(5)$$

$$= 40 \text{ cm}^2$$

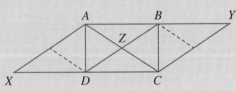

The following diagram shows 4 points:

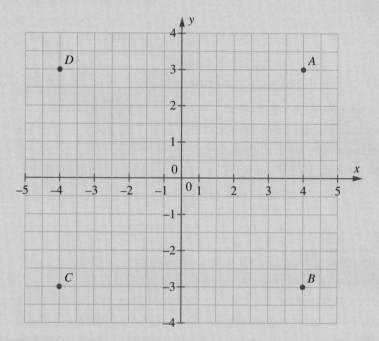

(i) List the coordinates of the points A, B, C and D.

Complete the following sentences:

(ii) B is the image of A under _____ .

(iii) C is the image of A under _____ .

(iv) D is the image of A under _____ .

Solution

(i) $A = (4, 3)$ $B = (4, -3)$ $C = (-4, -3)$ and $D = (-4, 3)$

(ii) B is the image of A under <u>axial symmetry in the x-axis.</u>

(iii) C is the image of A under <u>central symmetry in the origin $(0, 0)$.</u>

(iv) D is the image of A under <u>axial symmetry in the y-axis.</u>

The diagram shows the octagon *ABCDEFGH*.
The diagonals of the octagon intersect at the
point *O*.

Find the image of the shaded triangle *ABO*
under each of the following transformations:

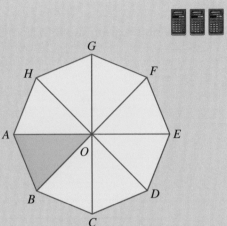

(i)   Axial symmetry in the line *AE*

(ii) Central symmetry in the point *O*

(iii) Axial symmetry in the line *GC*

(iv) Axial symmetry in the line *BF*

(v)   Name the transformation which maps
      the shaded triangle *ABO* onto Δ*GFO*.

Solution

(i)   Under axial symmetry in the line *AE*: Δ*ABO* → Δ*AHO*

(ii) Under central symmetry in point *O*: Δ*ABO* → Δ*EFO*

(iii) Under axial symmetry in the line *GC*: Δ*ABO* → Δ*EDO*

(iv) Under axial symmetry in the line *BF*: Δ*ABO* → Δ*CBO*

(v)   Δ*ABO* → Δ*GFO* is the result of a transformation under axial symmetry
      in the line *HD*.

key point

You should notice that in each case the image of the point *O* remained at the
point *O*. This is because in each transformation the point *O* was on the line or
point of symmetry.

5 Trigonometry I

☐ To learn how to use Pythagoras' theorem

☐ To learn how to label the sides of a right-angled triangle

☐ To learn how to use the trigonometric ratios to solve for missing sides and missing angles in right-angled triangles

For the Junior Certificate Higher Level trigonometry course, we will be working with right-angled triangles only. A right angle can be indicated by either a box or an L shape.

key point

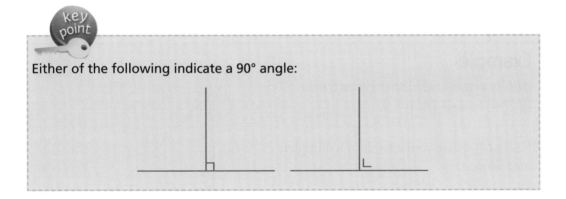

Either of the following indicate a 90° angle:

Pythagoras' theorem

Pythagoras' theorem states that, in a right-angled triangle, the square of the hypotenuse equals the sum of the squares of the other two sides.

Pythagoras' theorem is used:

1. To find the third side in a triangle, when given the other two sides
2. To verify that a triangle is right angled.

key point

The hypotenuse is always the longest side, facing the right angle.

(*see* booklet of formulae and tables page 16)

Pythagoras' theorem:

$$c^2 = a^2 + b^2$$

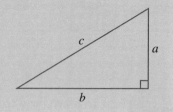

You must be able to prove Pythagoras' theorem. Refer to Chapter 2 on Geometry Theorems for the proof.

Example

ABC is a right-angled triangle such that $|AC| = 12$ and $|BC| = 9$.

Find $|AB|$. Leave your answer in its simplest surd form.

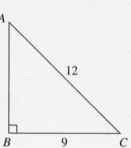

key point

Leaving your answer in surd form means there will be square roots in your answer.

Solution

Use Pythagoras' theorem:
$$c^2 = a^2 + b^2$$
$$(12)^2 = (9)^2 + |AB|^2$$
$$144 = 81 + |AB|^2$$
$$63 = |AB|^2$$
$$\sqrt{63} = |AB|$$
$$\sqrt{9}\sqrt{7} = |AB|$$
$$3\sqrt{7} = |AB|$$

key point

The hypotenuse side is always on its own on the left side of the equation.

PQR is an isosceles triangle with $|PQ| = |QR|$.
$|PR| = \sqrt{50}$ and $|\angle PQR| = 90°$.

Find $|PQ|$.

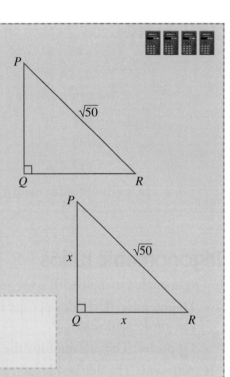

Solution

Let $|PQ| = |QR| = x$

Use Pythagoras' theorem:

$$c^2 = a^2 + b^2$$
$$(\sqrt{50})^2 = x^2 + x^2$$
$$50 = 2x^2$$
$$25 = x^2$$
$$\sqrt{25} = x$$
$$5 = x$$
$$\therefore |PQ| = 5$$

key point

Remember:

$(\sqrt{x})^2 = x$

The isosceles triangle shown in the diagram has a base length of 10 cm and the other two sides are 13 cm in length.

(i) Prove that the perpendicular line divides the isosceles triangle into two congruent triangles.

(ii) Hence, find, h, the perpendicular height of the triangle.

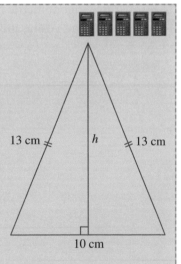

13 cm h 13 cm

10 cm

Solution

(i) The perpendicular height, h, cuts the big triangle into two smaller right-angled triangles.

Within these triangles:

$13 = 13$	(isosceles triangle)
$h = h$	(common side)
$90° = 90°$	(right angles)

Therefore, the triangles are congruent (RHS).

(ii) Since triangles are congruent, base of each triangle is 5 cm.
  Using Pythagoras' theorem on one of these triangles:

$$c^2 = a^2 + b^2$$
$$13^2 = h^2 + 5^2$$
$$169 = h^2 + 25$$
$$144 = h^2$$
$$\sqrt{144} = h$$
$$12 = h$$

Therefore, perpendicular height, $h = 12$ cm.

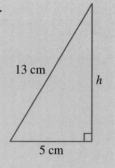

Trigonometric ratios

In a right-angled triangle with acute angle θ, we name the sides as:

- **Hypotenuse:** The side opposite the right angle. It is also the longest side.
- **Opposite:** The side opposite the angle θ.
- **Adjacent:** The side beside (adjacent to) θ.

Note: θ is a Greek letter, pronounced 'theta', which is often used to denote an angle.

There are three trigonometric ratios. These ratios are fractions, with one side over another. They are called sine, cosine and tangent and are usually abbreviated to sin, cos and tan.

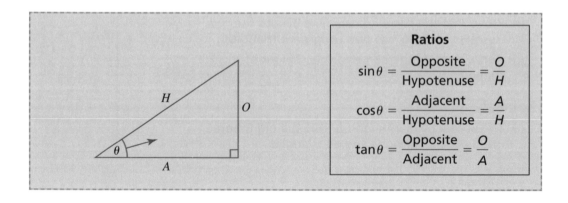

Ratios

$$\sin\theta = \frac{\text{Opposite}}{\text{Hypotenuse}} = \frac{O}{H}$$

$$\cos\theta = \frac{\text{Adjacent}}{\text{Hypotenuse}} = \frac{A}{H}$$

$$\tan\theta = \frac{\text{Opposite}}{\text{Adjacent}} = \frac{O}{A}$$

Memory aids

1. O Hell, Another Hour Of Algebra:

2. Silly $= \dfrac{\text{Old}}{\text{Harry}}$ Caught $= \dfrac{\text{A}}{\text{Herring}}$ Trawling $= \dfrac{\text{Off}}{\text{America}}$

3. SOHCAHTOA

Using the calculator

You must be able to use your calculator to find the value for the sin, cos and tan of angles. Your calculator is able to work in many different modes. Because of this, you **must make sure your calculator is set to do calculations in degrees**, at all times.

Example

Use your calculator to show that $\tan 70° \neq \tan 80° - \tan 10°$

Solution

Use the calculator to evaluate:

$$\tan 70° = 2{\cdot}747 \quad \tan 80° = 5{\cdot}671 \quad \tan 10° = 0{\cdot}176$$

Does $\tan 70° = \tan 80° - \tan 10°$?

LHS	RHS
$\tan 70°$	$\tan 80° - \tan 10°$
$2{\cdot}747$	$5{\cdot}671 - 0{\cdot}176$
	$5{\cdot}495$

$$\text{LHS} \neq \text{RHS}$$

Therefore, $\tan 70° \neq \tan 80° - \tan 10°$

Example

Use page 13 of the booklet of formulae and tables to show that
$$\sin 90° \neq \sin 60° + \sin 30°$$

Solution

Using page 13 of the booklet of formula and tables, evaluate:

$$\sin 90° = 1 \qquad \sin 60° = \frac{\sqrt{3}}{2} \qquad \sin 30° = \frac{1}{2}$$

Does $\sin 90° = \sin 60° + \sin 30°$?

LHS	RHS
$\sin 90°$	$\sin 60° + \sin 30°$
1	$\dfrac{\sqrt{3}}{2} + \dfrac{1}{2}$
	$\dfrac{\sqrt{3} + 1}{2}$

$$\text{LHS} \neq \text{RHS}$$
Therefore, $\sin 90° \neq \sin 60° + \sin 30°$

Example

Without using a calculator, construct the angle A such that
$$2 \tan A = 7, \qquad 0° \leq A \leq 90°.$$

Solution

$$2 \tan A = 7$$

$$\tan A = \frac{7}{2} = \frac{\text{opp}}{\text{adj}} \qquad \text{(divide both sides by 2)}$$

Construct the triangle with angle A,
where opposite side = 7 and the adjacent side = 2:

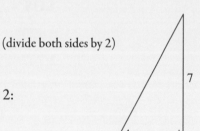

Example

If $\sin B = \dfrac{8}{17}$, without finding the value for B, find $\cos B$ and $\tan B$ in rational (fraction) form.

Solution

$$\sin B = \frac{8}{17} = \frac{\text{opp}}{\text{hyp}}$$

Construct the triangle with angle B, where opposite side $= 8$ and the hypotenuse $= 17$.
Use Pythagoras' theorem to find the missing side:

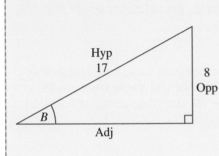

$$(\text{hyp})^2 = (\text{opp})^2 + (\text{adj})^2$$
$$17^2 = 8^2 + (\text{adj})^2$$
$$289 = 64 + (\text{adj})^2$$
$$225 = (\text{adj})^2$$
$$15 = \text{adj}$$

$$\cos B = \frac{\text{adj}}{\text{hyp}} \qquad \tan B = \frac{\text{opp}}{\text{adj}}$$

$$\cos B = \frac{15}{17} \qquad \tan B = \frac{8}{15}$$

 exam Q

During a trigonometry lesson, a group of students made some predictions about what they expected to find for the values of the trigonometric functions of some angles. They then found the sine, cosine and tangent of 25° and 50°.

(i) In the table given, show, correct to three decimal places, the values they found.

$\sin 25° =$	$\cos 25° =$	$\tan 25° =$
$\sin 50° =$	$\cos 50° =$	$\tan 50° =$

(ii) (a) Maria had said, "The value from any of these trigonometric functions will always be less than 1." Was Maria correct? Give a reason for your answer.

(b) Sharon had said, "If the size of the angle is doubled, then the value from any of these trigonometric functions will also double." Was Sharon correct? Give a reason for your answer.

(c) James had said, "The value for all of these trigonometric functions will increase if the size of the angle is increased." Was James correct? Give a reason for your answer.

Solution

(i) Completing the table with answers to three decimal places:

$\sin 25° = 0{\cdot}423$	$\cos 25° = 0{\cdot}906$	$\tan 25° = 0{\cdot}466$
$\sin 50° = 0{\cdot}766$	$\cos 50° = 0{\cdot}643$	$\tan 50° = 1{\cdot}192$

(ii) (a) No, Maria was not correct.

The value for $\tan 50° = 1{\cdot}192$ which is greater than 1, therefore the value from any of these trigonometric functions will not always be less than 1.

(b) No, Sharon was not correct.

In each case, doubling the angle did not result in the value for the trigonometric function doubling. For example, the value for $\sin 50° = 0{\cdot}766$ is not twice the value for $\sin 25° = 0{\cdot}423$.

(c) No, James was not correct.

James' statement is correct for the sine and tangent functions, but in the case of the cosine function, increasing the size of the angle from $\cos 25° = 0{\cdot}906$ to $\cos 50° = 0{\cdot}643$, reduced the value for the trigonometric function.

key point

For an acute angle θ:
- The biggest value that $\sin \theta$ and $\cos \theta$ can ever be is 1.
- $\tan \theta$ can be any value, up to infinity.

exam Q

(i) Construct a right-angled triangle containing an angle A, such that $\sin A = 0{\cdot}4$.

(ii) Find, from your triangle, $\cos A$ in surd form.

Solution

(i) $\sin A = 0{\cdot}4$

$$\therefore \sin A = \frac{2}{5} = \frac{\text{opp}}{\text{hyp}} \qquad \left(\text{Since } 0{\cdot}4 = \frac{4}{10} = \frac{2}{5} \right)$$

Construct the triangle with angle A, where opposite side = 2 and hypotenuse = 5.

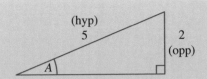

(ii) To find cos A, we need the adjacent side.
Use Pythagoras' theorem to find the adjacent:

$$(\text{hyp})^2 = (\text{opp})^2 + (\text{adj})^2 \qquad\qquad \cos A = \dfrac{\text{adj}}{\text{hyp}}$$

$$(5)^2 = (2)^2 + (\text{adj})^2$$

$$25 = 4 + (\text{adj})^2 \qquad\qquad\qquad \therefore \cos A = \dfrac{\sqrt{21}}{5}$$

$$21 = (\text{adj})^2$$

$$\sqrt{21} = \text{adj}$$

exam Q

If $\tan A = \dfrac{1}{3}$, find the value of $\sin^2 A + \cos^2 A$.

Solution

$$\tan A = \frac{1}{3} = \frac{\text{opp}}{\text{adj}}$$

Construct the triangle with angle A, where opposite side = 1 and adjacent side = 3.

Use Pythagoras' theorem to find the third side:

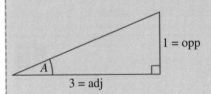

$$(\text{hyp})^2 = (\text{opp})^2 + (\text{adj})^2$$

$$(\text{hyp})^2 = (1)^2 + (3)^2$$

$$(\text{hyp})^2 = 1 + 9$$

$$(\text{hyp})^2 = 10$$

$$\text{hyp} = \sqrt{10}$$

$$\sin A = \frac{\text{opp}}{\text{hyp}} \Rightarrow \sin A = \frac{1}{\sqrt{10}}$$

$$\cos A = \frac{\text{adj}}{\text{hyp}} \Rightarrow \cos A = \frac{3}{\sqrt{10}}$$

$$\sin^2 A + \cos^2 A = \left(\frac{1}{\sqrt{10}}\right)^2 + \left(\frac{3}{\sqrt{10}}\right)^2$$

$$\sin^2 A + \cos^2 A = \frac{1}{10} + \frac{9}{10}$$

$$\sin^2 A + \cos^2 A = \frac{10}{10}$$

$$\sin^2 A + \cos^2 A = 1$$

Note: this formula can be found in the booklet of formulae and tables, page 13.

Using trigonometric ratios to find missing sides or angles in a triangle

To use the trigonometric formula to find a missing side, or a missing angle, in a triangle, follow these steps:

1. Label the sides of the triangle.
2. Write down what information you have and what information you want.
3. Select which formula to use.
4. Substitute values into the formula.
5. Solve the resulting equation to find the missing value.

For each question, write out what information you have and what information you want. This will help you to figure out which formula to use. Learn the above steps.

Example

ABC is a right-angled triangle.
$|\angle ACB| = 50°$ and $|AC| = 10$ cm.

Calculate the length of $[AB]$, correct to two decimal places.

Solution

Label the sides.
We have the hypotenuse and we want the opposite.

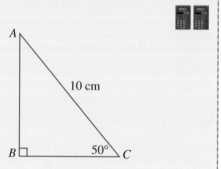

Therefore, use the formula:

$$\sin\theta = \frac{\text{opp}}{\text{hyp}}$$

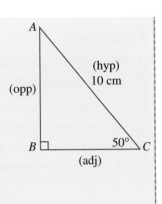

$$\sin 50° = \frac{|AB|}{10}$$ (substitute in known values)

$$10\sin 50° = |AB|$$ (multiply both sides by 10)

$$7{\cdot}66044 = |AB|$$ (use your calculator to evaluate $10\sin 50°$)

$$7{\cdot}66 = |AB|$$ to two decimal places

Example

ABC is a right-angled triangle.
$|\angle BAC| = 35°$ and $|AB| = 8$ cm.

Calculate the length of $[AC]$,
correct to two decimal places.

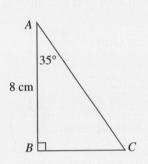

Solution

Label the sides.

We have the adjacent and we want the hypotenuse.
Therefore, use the formula:

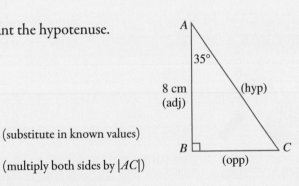

$$\cos\theta = \frac{\text{adj}}{\text{hyp}}$$

$$\cos 35° = \frac{8}{|AC|}$$ (substitute in known values)

$$|AC|\cos 35° = 8$$ (multiply both sides by $|AC|$)

$$|AC| = \frac{8}{\cos 35°}$$ (divide both sides by $\cos 35°$)

$$|AC| = 9{\cdot}76619$$ $\left(\text{use your calculator to evaluate } \dfrac{8}{\cos 35°}\right)$

$$|AC| = 9{\cdot}77$$ to two decimal places

Example

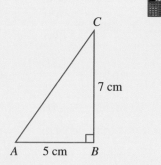

ABC is a right-angled triangle.

$|BC| = 7$ cm and $|AB| = 5$ cm.

Find $|\angle ACB|$:

(i) correct to one place of decimal

(ii) in degrees and minutes, correct to the nearest minute.

Solution

Mark in the required angle and, hence, label the sides.

We have the adjacent and the opposite. Therefore, use the formula:

$$\tan\theta = \frac{\text{opp}}{\text{adj}}$$

$$\tan|\angle ACB| = \frac{5}{7} \qquad \text{(substitute in known values)}$$

$$|\angle ACB| = \tan^{-1}\left(\frac{5}{7}\right) \qquad \text{(apply } \tan^{-1} \text{ to both sides)}$$

$$|\angle ACB| = 35{\cdot}537° \qquad \left(\text{use your calculator to evaluate } \tan^{-1}\left(\frac{5}{7}\right)\right)$$

(i) $\angle ACB = 35{\cdot}5°$ to one decimal place

(ii) $\angle ACB = 35° \, 32'$ to the nearest minute

You can use the degree (DMS) button on your calculator to convert angles from decimal to degrees, minutes and seconds (DMS) format.

Remember:

60 seconds = 1 minute

60 minutes = 1 degree

Example

In the triangle shown:

(i) Calculate k, and leave your answer in the form $\dfrac{a}{\sqrt{b}}$, where $a, b \in \mathbb{N}$.

(ii) Calculate the area of the triangle.

Give both answers in surd form.

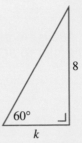

Solution

(i) Label the sides of the triangle:

Opposite side = 8

Adjacent side = k

Angle = 60°

Therefore, use the formula: $\tan \theta = \dfrac{\text{opp}}{\text{adj}}$

$\tan 60° = \dfrac{8}{k}$ (substitute in known values)

$k (\tan 60°) = 8$ (multiply both sides by k)

$k = \dfrac{8}{\tan 60°}$ (divide both sides by tan 60°)

$k = \dfrac{8}{\sqrt{3}}$ (use your calculator to find tan 60°)

(ii) Area of triangle $= \dfrac{1}{2}(\text{base}) \times (\text{height})$

$\qquad\qquad\quad = \dfrac{1}{2}\left(\dfrac{8\sqrt{3}}{3}\right) \times (8)$

$\qquad\qquad\quad = \dfrac{32\sqrt{3}}{3}$ sq. units   (use your calculator to simplify the expression)

In the diagram, *ABC* is a right-angled triangle, with *AC* perpendicular to *BC*. $|AC| = 2\sqrt{2}$ and $|BC| = 3\sqrt{3}$.

Calculate:

(i) $|AB|$, leaving your answer in surd form

(ii) $|\angle ABC|$, correct to the nearest degree.

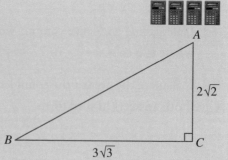

Solution

(i) Using Pythagoras' theorem:

$$c^2 = a^2 + b^2$$

$$|AB|^2 = (2\sqrt{2})^2 + (3\sqrt{3})^2$$

$$|AB|^2 = 8 + 27$$

$$|AB|^2 = 35$$

$$|AB| = \sqrt{35}$$

key point

Use Pythagoras' theorem when you have two sides of a right-angled triangle, and need to find the third side.

(ii) Mark $\angle ABC$ on the triangle and, hence, label the sides:

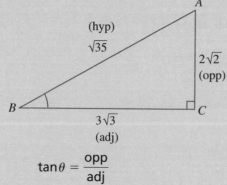

exam focus

We have all three sides of the triangle, so we can use any of the three trigonometric ratios to solve for the angle. However, it is wise not to use $|AB|$, in case we made an error in (i).

$$\tan\theta = \frac{\text{opp}}{\text{adj}}$$

$$\tan\angle ABC = \frac{2\sqrt{2}}{3\sqrt{3}} \qquad \text{(substitute in the known values)}$$

$$\angle ABC = \tan^{-1}\left(\frac{2\sqrt{2}}{3\sqrt{3}}\right) \qquad \text{(apply } \tan^{-1} \text{ to both sides)}$$

$$\angle ABC = 28 \cdot 56° \qquad \left(\text{use your calculator to evaluate } \tan^{-1}\left(\frac{2\sqrt{2}}{3\sqrt{3}}\right)\right)$$

$$\angle ABC = 29° \qquad \text{(to the nearest degree)}$$

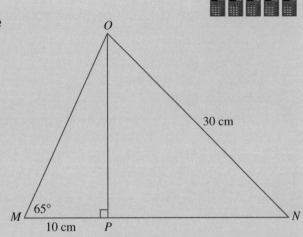

In the diagram, *MNO* is a triangle with [*OP*] perpendicular to [*MN*].

|*MP*| = 10 cm, |*ON*| = 30 cm and |∠*PMO*| = 65°

Calculate:

(i) |*OP*|, correct to one decimal place

(ii) |∠*MON*|, correct to the nearest degree.

Solution

(i) Look at Δ*MPO*:

Label the sides, in relation to the 65° angle.

We have the adjacent and we want the opposite. Therefore, use the formula:

$$\tan\theta = \frac{opp}{adj}$$

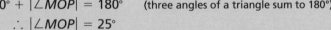

$$\tan 65° = \frac{|OP|}{10}$$ (substitute in the known values)

$10 \tan 65° = |OP|$ (multiply both sides by 10)

$21·445 = |OP|$ (use calculator to evaluate 10 tan65°)

$21·4$ cm $= |OP|$ (to one decimal place)

(ii) To find |∠*MON*| we need |∠*MOP*| and |∠*PON*|.

In Δ*MPO*: 65° + 90° + |∠*MOP*| = 180°   (three angles of a triangle sum to 180°)

∴ |∠*MOP*| = 25°

Enter |∠*MOP*| and |*OP*| on the diagram. In Δ*PON*, label the sides in relation to ∠*PON*.

We have the adjacent and the hypotenuse. Therefore, use the formula:

$$\cos\theta = \frac{adj}{hyp}$$

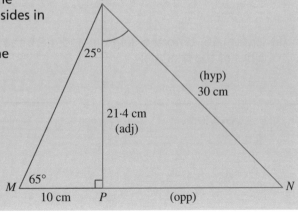

$$\cos|\angle PON| = \frac{21\cdot4}{30} \qquad \text{(substitute in the known values)}$$

$$|\angle PON| = \cos^{-1}\left(\frac{21\cdot4}{30}\right) \quad \text{(apply } \cos^{-1} \text{ to both sides)}$$

$$|\angle PON| = 44\cdot49°$$

$$|\angle MON| = |\angle MOP| + |\angle PON|$$

$$|\angle MON| = 25° + 44\cdot49°$$

$$|\angle MON| = 69\cdot49°$$

$$|\angle MON| = 69° \qquad \text{(to the nearest degree)}$$

key point

Remember to round down if there is less than 0·5 after the whole number part.

exam Q

In the triangle ABC, $|AB| = 2$ and $|BC| = 1$.

(i) Find $|AC|$, giving your answer in surd form.

(ii) Write $\cos\angle BAC$ as a ratio and, hence, find $|\angle BAC|$.

(iii) Sketch a right-angled isosceles triangle in which the equal sides are 1 unit each and use it to write $\cos45°$ in surd form.

(iv) Show that $\cos75° \neq \cos45° + \cos30°$.

Solution

(i) Enter the given information onto the diagram.

Using Pythagoras' theorem:

$$|AB|^2 = |BC|^2 + |AC|^2$$

$$2^2 = 1^2 + |AC|^2$$

$$4 = 1 + |AC|^2$$

$$3 = |AC|^2$$

$$\sqrt{3} = |AC|$$

(ii) Enter $|AC|$ onto the diagram and mark the angle $\angle BAC$. Hence, label the sides of the triangle:

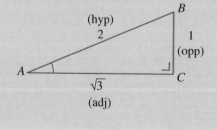

$$\cos\theta = \frac{\text{adj}}{\text{hyp}}$$

$$\cos\angle BAC = \frac{\sqrt{3}}{2}$$

$$\angle BAC = \cos^{-1}\left(\frac{\sqrt{3}}{2}\right)$$

$$\angle BAC = 30°$$

(iii) Isosceles triangle with the equal sides 1 unit in length:

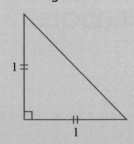

Find the missing side:

$$c^2 = a^2 + b^2$$
$$c^2 = 1^2 + 1^2$$
$$c^2 = 1 + 1$$
$$c^2 = 2$$
$$c = \sqrt{2}$$

Enter the value for the hypotenuse.

Enter the two angles: they are 45° each
(since the triangle is right angled and isosceles).

Mark one of the 45° angles and label the sides:

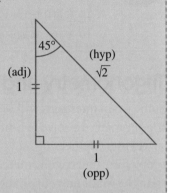

$$\cos\theta = \frac{adj}{hyp}$$

$$\cos45° = \frac{1}{\sqrt{2}}$$

(iv) To show that $\cos75° \neq \cos45° + \cos30°$:

Evaluate the left-hand side:

$$\cos75°$$

$$\frac{\sqrt{6} - \sqrt{2}}{4}$$

$$0.2588190451$$

Evaluate the right-hand side:

$$\cos45° + \cos30°$$

$$\frac{1}{\sqrt{2}} + \frac{\sqrt{3}}{2} \qquad \text{(from (ii) and (iiii))}$$

$$\frac{\sqrt{3} + \sqrt{2}}{2}$$

$$1.573132185$$

The left-hand side does not equal the right-hand side.

∴ cos 75° ≠ cos 45° + cos 30°

6 Trigonometry II: Real Life Applications

aims
- ☐ To learn how to solve triangles from in-context situations to find missing sides or angles
- ☐ To learn how to find the area of a triangle, from in-context situations
- ☐ To learn how to solve trigonometric equations, from in-context situations

Trigonometry and geometry in context

Some exam questions will require you to combine your knowledge of geometry and trigonometry to solve real-life problems. Many practical problems in navigation, surveying, engineering and geography involve solving a triangle. When solving practical problems using trigonometry in this course, represent each situation with a right-angled triangle. Mark on your triangle the angles and lengths you know and label what you need to calculate, using the correct ratio to link the angle or length required with the known angle or length.

key point

When a question involves a vertical object, such as a tree, tower, building, cliff, etc., we can assume that a right angle is formed between the vertical object and the ground.

exam focus

It is very important to draw a sketch of the problem. This will help you to visualise the problem and hopefully lead you to a solution.

Angles of elevation and depression and compass directions

Angle of elevation

The **angle of elevation** of an object as seen by an observer is the angle between the horizontal line from the object to the observer's line of vision (upwards from the horizontal).

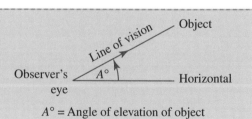

$A°$ = Angle of elevation of object

Angle of depression

If the object is below the level of the observer, the angle between the horizontal and the observer's line of vision is called the **angle of depression** (downwards from the horizontal).

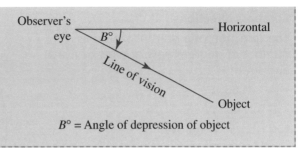

$B°$ = Angle of depression of object

key point

An angle of elevation has an equal angle of depression. The angle of elevation from A to B is equal to the angle of depression from B to A.

The angles are alternate angles, as the horizontal lines are parallel, as indicated by the arrow symbols.

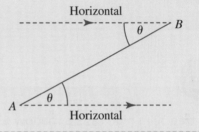

exam focus

It is important for you to be familiar with a **clinometer**. A clinometer is a device used to measure angles of elevation and/or angles of depression.

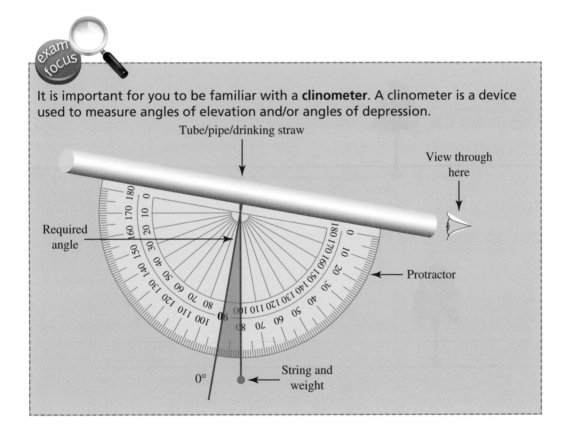

Compass directions

The direction of a point is stated as a number of degrees east or west of north and south.

- *A* is N 60° E
- *B* is N 40° W
- *C* is S 45° W (or SW)
- *D* is S 70° E

Note: N 60° E means start at north and turn 60° towards east.

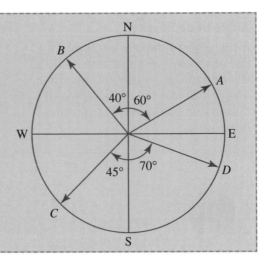

A tree 32 m high casts a shadow 63 m long. Calculate θ, the angle of elevation of the sun. Give your answer in degrees and minutes (correct to the nearest minute).

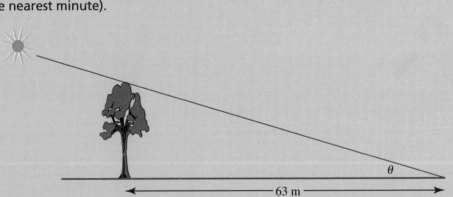

Solution

Enter the height of the tree. Label the sides in relation to the angle of elevation:

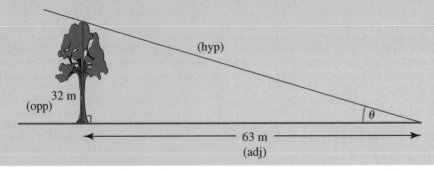

$$\tan\theta = \frac{\text{opp}}{\text{adj}}$$

$$\tan\theta = \frac{32}{63}$$

$$\theta = \tan^{-1}\left(\frac{32}{63}\right)$$

$$\theta = 26\cdot927°$$

$$\theta = 26° \ 55' \ 39''$$

Therefore, the angle of elevation is 26° 56', to the nearest minute.

exam focus

Remember there are 60 seconds in 1 minute.

exam Q

A homeowner wishes to remove the three identical steps leading to her front door and to replace them with a ramp.

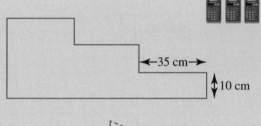

←35 cm→

↕10 cm

Each step is 10 cm high and 35 cm long.

ramp

Find the length of the ramp.
Give your answer correct to one decimal place.

Solution

Each step is 10 cm high, so the ramp must reach a height of 10 × 3 = 30 cm.
Each step is 35 cm long, so the ramp must cover a width of 35 × 3 = 105 cm across.
Use Pythagoras' theorem to find the length of the ramp:

$$c^2 = a^2 + b^2$$

$$(\text{ramp})^2 = (30)^2 + (105)^2$$

$$(\text{ramp})^2 = 900 + 11{,}025$$

$$(\text{ramp})^2 = 11{,}925$$

$$\text{ramp} = \sqrt{11{,}925}$$

$$\text{ramp} = 109\cdot2016$$

Therefore, ramp = 109·2 cm in length.

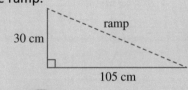

30 cm

ramp

105 cm

key point

Where it applies, we can assume the angles are 90°.

Example

The diagram shows an office block
built on a river bank. From a point on
the opposite river bank, the angle of
elevation of the top of the office block
is 30°.

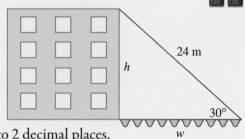

(i) Find h, the height of the office block.

(ii) Find w, the width of the river, correct to 2 decimal places.

Solution

(i) Redraw the triangle and label the sides, in relation to the 30° angle.

To find h:

We have the hypotenuse = 24 m and we want the opposite = h. Therefore,
use the formula:

$$\sin\theta = \frac{\text{opp}}{\text{hyp}}$$

$$\sin 30° = \frac{h}{24}$$

$$24\sin 30° = h$$

$$12 = h$$

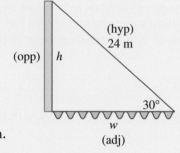

Therefore, the height of the building is 12 m.

(ii) Redraw the triangle and label the sides, in relation to the 30° angle.

To find w:

We have the hypotenuse = 24 m and we want the adjacent = w. Therefore,
use the formula:

$$\cos\theta = \frac{\text{adj}}{\text{hyp}}$$

$$\cos 30° = \frac{w}{24}$$

$$24\cos 30° = w$$

$$12\sqrt{3} = w$$

$$20{\cdot}78 = w$$

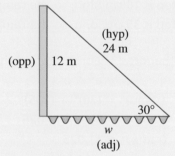

Therefore, the width of the river is 20·78 m.

Example

Sally has measured the shadow cast by the blue spruce tree in her family's front yard to be about 22 metres. She estimates that the angle of elevation when she is standing at the end of the shadow to the top of the blue spruce to be 55°.

  (i) Make a sketch of the situation.
 (ii) Find the height of the tree, correct to one place of decimal.
(iii) Find the distance Sally is from the top of the tree, correct to two decimal places.

Solution

  (i) Sketch:

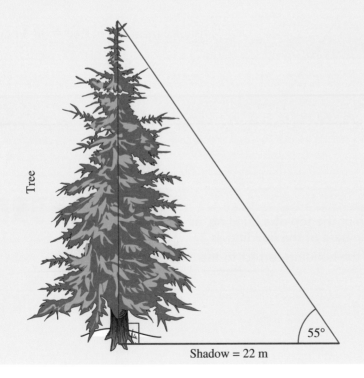

Tree

55°

Shadow = 22 m

(ii) To find height of tree:

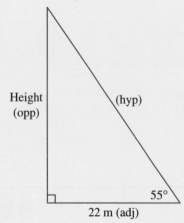

$$\tan A = \frac{opp}{adj}$$

$$\tan 55° = \frac{height}{22}$$

$$22 \tan 55° = height$$

$$31\cdot4 \text{ m} = height$$

(iii) To find distance Sally is from the top of the tree:

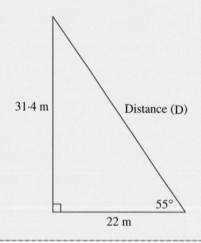

$$(Hyp)^2 = (Opp)^2 + (Adj)^2$$
$$D^2 = (31\cdot4)^2 + (22)^2$$
$$D^2 = 985\cdot96 + 484$$
$$D^2 = 1,469\cdot96$$
$$D = 38\cdot34$$

Distance from top of tree $= 38\cdot34$ m

exam Q

The angle of elevation of the top of a building, as viewed from a point A, 81 m from the base of the building, is 27°.

(i) Find the height of the building correct to the nearest metre.

(ii) The bottom of a balloon is 62 m above the top of the building, as shown. Find the angle of elevation of the bottom of the balloon as viewed from the point A. Give your answer correct to the nearest degree.

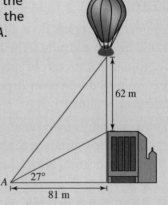

Solution

(i) Look at the small triangle. Label the sides in relation to the 27° angle.

We want the opposite and we have the adjacent = 81. Therefore, use the formula:

$$\tan\theta = \frac{opp}{adj}$$

$$\tan 27° = \frac{opp}{81}$$

$$81\tan 27° = opp$$

$$41\cdot27 = opp$$

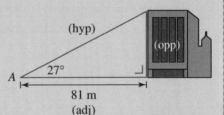

Therefore, the height of the building = 41 m.

(ii) Look at the large triangle:

The height of the balloon is 62 + 41 = 103 m

Label the sides in relation to the angle of elevation.

We want the ∠A and we have the opposite = 103 and we have the adjacent = 81. Therefore, use the formula:

$$\tan\theta = \frac{opp}{adj}$$

$$\tan\theta = \frac{103}{81}$$

$$\theta = \tan^{-1}\left(\frac{103}{81}\right)$$

$$\theta = 51\cdot81°$$

Therefore, the angle of elevation = 52°.

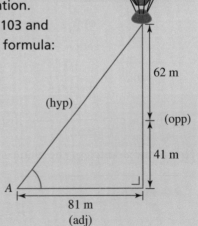

Example

Commercial aircrafts fly at altitudes of between 9,000 m and 11,000 m. The altitude is the height the aircraft is **directly** above the ground. An aircraft begins its gradual descent a long distance away from its destination airport. We will assume that the path of descent is a line.

(i) An aircraft is flying at an altitude of 10,000 m and the angle of descent is 2°. At what distance, to the nearest km, from the destination runway should the descent begin? [Note: the required distance is the horizontal distance along the ground.]

(ii) An aircraft is flying at an altitude of 9·3 km. A passenger becomes ill and the pilot needs to land at the nearest airport which is 200 km away. Find the angle of descent, correct to two decimal places.

Solution

(i) Change 10,000 m into 10 km.

Draw a diagram of the plane coming in for landing. The angle on the ground is alternate to the angle of descent, so the angle on the ground is 2°.

key point

1,000 m = 1 km

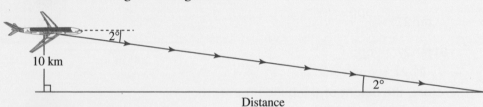

We have the opposite = 10 km and we want the adjacent. Therefore, use the formula:

$$\tan\theta = \frac{\text{opp}}{\text{adj}}$$

$$\tan 2° = \frac{10}{\text{distance}}$$

$$\text{distance} = \frac{10}{\tan 2°} \implies \text{distance} = 286 \text{ km} \qquad \text{(to the nearest km)}$$

opp = 10

adj = D

(ii) Draw a sketch of the plane coming in for landing:

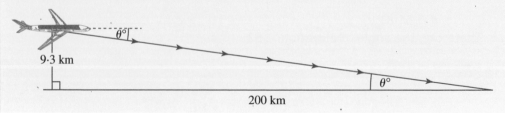

9·3 km

200 km

$$\tan\theta = \frac{\text{opp}}{\text{adj}}$$

$$\tan\theta = \frac{9\cdot3}{200}$$

$$\tan\theta = 0\cdot0465 \quad \Rightarrow \quad \theta = 2\cdot66°$$

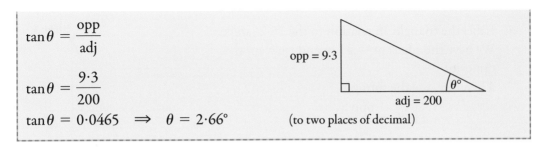

opp = 9·3

adj = 200

$\theta°$

(to two places of decimal)

Example

A tree on one side of a river is due west of a rock on the other side of the river. From a stake, 21 m north of the rock, the bearing of the tree is S 25·2° W.

(i) Draw a diagram to represent the given information.

(ii) Hence, find the distance from rock to the tree. Give your answer to one decimal place.

Solution

(i) Diagram:

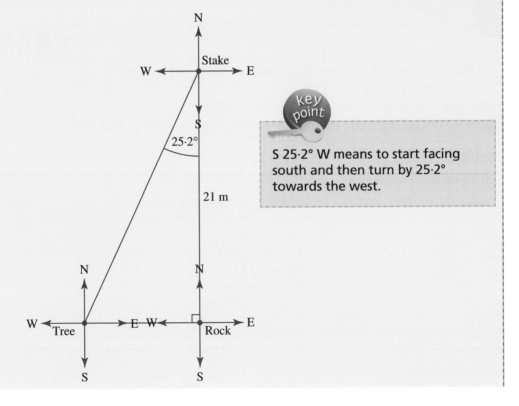

key point

S 25·2° W means to start facing south and then turn by 25·2° towards the west.

(ii) Label the triangle, in relation to the 25·2° angle.
We have the adjacent = 21 m and we want the
opposite.
Therefore, use the formula:

$$\tan \theta = \frac{opp}{adj}$$

$$\tan 25 \cdot 2° = \frac{opp}{21}$$

$$21(\tan 25 \cdot 2°) = opp$$

$$9 \cdot 88 = opp$$

Therefore, the distance from the tree to the
rock is 9·9 m.

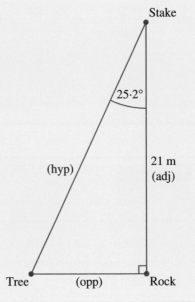

exam
Q

Two ships leave a port, *P*, at 11:00. Ship *A* sails in the direction
N 42° E at a speed of 12 km/h. Ship *B* sails in the direction S 48° E
at a speed of 15 km/h.

 (i) Draw a diagram to represent this information.
(ii) How far apart are the ships at 15:30? Give your answer to two decimal places.

Solution
(i) Diagram:

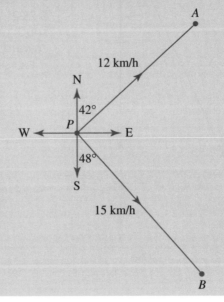

(ii) The ships have been travelling for:

15:30 − 11:00 = 4 hours 30 minutes = 4·5 hours

Ship A: Distance = Speed × Time

Distance = 12 × 4·5 = 54 km

Ship B: Distance = Speed × Time

Distance = 15 × 4·5 = 67·5 km

Filling in the missing angles at the point P results in a right-angled triangle.

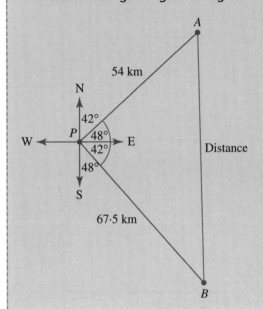

key point

Remember the formulae which relate distance, speed and time:

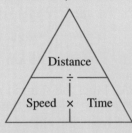

Use Pythagoras' theorem:

$$c^2 = a^2 + b^2$$
$$(\text{distance})^2 = (54)^2 + (67·5)^2$$
$$(\text{distance})^2 = 2{,}916 + 4{,}556·25$$
$$(\text{distance})^2 = 7{,}472·25$$
$$\text{distance} = \sqrt{7{,}472·25}$$
$$\text{distance} = 86·44 \text{ km}$$

Therefore, the ships will be 86·44 km apart at 15:30.

exam Q

In the diagram, PQRS represents the course of a triathlon. Competitors must swim the 9 km from P to Q, then run the 12 km from Q to R and cycle from R to S and then cycle back to P. $|\angle PSR| = 36·87°$

(i) Find the distance from P to R.

(ii) Find the distance from R to S, to the nearest kilometre.

(iii) Hence, find the length of the entire course.

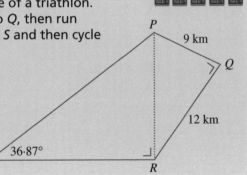

Solution

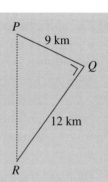

(i) Use Pythagoras' theorem on $\triangle PQR$ to find $|PR|$:

$$c^2 = a^2 + b^2$$
$$|PR|^2 = (9)^2 + (12)^2$$
$$|PR|^2 = 81 + 144$$
$$|PR|^2 = 225$$
$$|PR| = \sqrt{225}$$
$$|PR| = 15 \text{ km}$$

(ii) In $\triangle PRS$, label the sides in relation to the $36 \cdot 87°$ angle. We have the opposite = 15 km and we want the adjacent. Therefore, use the formula:

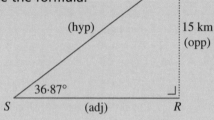

$$\tan\theta = \frac{\text{opp}}{\text{adj}}$$

$$\tan 36 \cdot 87° = \frac{15}{|SR|}$$

$$|SR| \tan 36 \cdot 87° = 15$$

$$|SR| = \frac{15}{\tan 36 \cdot 87°}$$

$$|SR| = 19 \cdot 9999$$

Therefore, $|SR| = 20$ km

(iii) To find the length of the entire course, we need $|SP|$. Use Pythagoras' theorem on $\triangle PRS$:

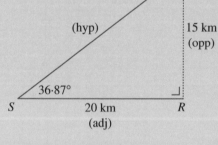

$$c^2 = a^2 + b^2$$
$$|PS|^2 = (20)^2 + (15)^2$$
$$|PS|^2 = 400 + 225$$
$$|PS|^2 = 625$$
$$|PS| = \sqrt{625}$$
$$|PS| = 25 \text{ km}$$

Length of the entire course is the total distance from P to Q to R to S and back up to P:

$$= 9 + 12 + 20 + 25$$
$$= 66 \text{ km}$$

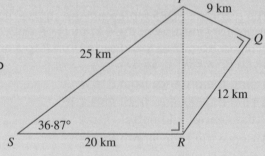

Seán makes a clinometer using a protractor, a straw, a piece of thread and a piece of plasticine (used as a weight). He stands 10 m from a tree and uses his clinometer to measure the angle of elevation to the top of the tree as shown. Seán is 1·75 m in height.

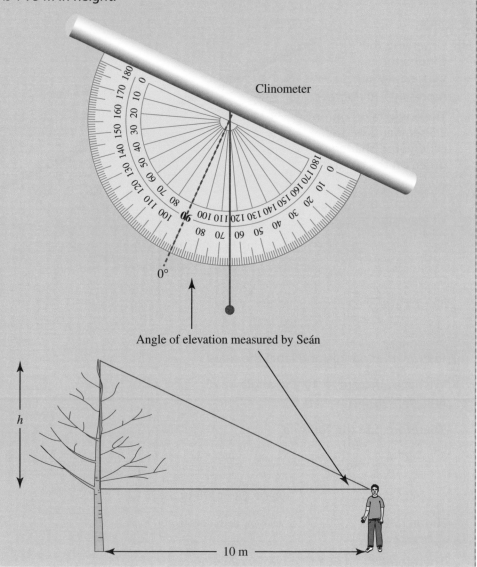

(i) Find the angle of elevation by reading the clinometer above.

(ii) Calculate the height, h, as shown in the diagram. Give your answer correct to two decimal places.

(iii) Find the total height of the tree.

(iv) Another student uses the same method as Seán and finds the height of the tree to be 23·1 m. Seán did not get this answer. Give one possible reason why the answers might be different.

Solution

(i) Observing the clinometer:

Each segment represents 10 degrees.

The angle takes up 2·5 segments on the clinometer (shaded in green on the diagram)

Therefore, the angle of elevation = 25°.

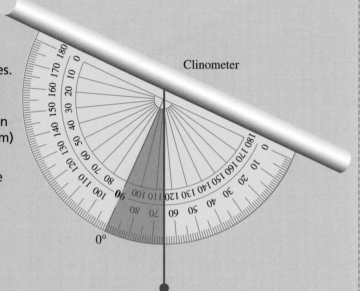

Clinometer

(ii) Redraw the triangle and label the sides:

We have adjacent = 10 and angle = 25° and want opposite = h.

Therefore, use the formula:

$$\tan\theta = \frac{\text{opp}}{\text{adj}}$$

$$\tan 25° = \frac{h}{10} \qquad \text{(put in known values)}$$

$$10(\tan 25°) = h \qquad \text{(multiply both sides by 10)}$$

$$4\cdot663 = h \qquad \text{(use calculator)}$$

Therefore, $h = 4\cdot66$ m, to two decimal places.

(iii) Height of the tree = Height of Seán + value for *h* (from part (ii)

Height of the tree = 1·75 + 4·66

Height of the tree = 6·41 m

(iv) The different answers may result from inaccuracy in measuring the height of the boys, the distance 10 m or the angle on the clinometer.

For example, the other boy may have measured the angle on the wrong side of the weight on the clinometer.

exam focus

In a recent exam, this question was very poorly answered. Consequently part (i) was awarded 10 marks. Parts (ii) and (iii) **together** were awarded a total of 5 marks and part (iv) was awarded 5 marks.

exam Q

A boat sails due east from the base *A* of a 30 m high lighthouse, [*AD*]. At the point *B*, the angle of depression of the boat from the top of the lighthouse is 68°. Ten seconds later the boat is at the point *C* and the angle of depression is now 33°.

(i) Find |*AB*|, to the nearest metre,

(ii) Find |*BC*|, the distance the boat has travelled in this time, to the nearest metre.

(iii) Calculate the average speed at which the boat is sailing between *B* and *C*. Give your answer in metres per second, correct to one decimal place.

30 m

D

A   B   C

Solution

(i) Mark in the angle of depression 68°. This equals the angle of elevation from *B* to the top of the lighthouse. Label the sides in the small triangle, in relation to the 68° angle.

We have the opposite = 30 m and we want the adjacent side.

Therefore, use the formula:

$$\tan\theta = \frac{\text{opp}}{\text{adj}}$$

$$\tan 68° = \frac{30}{|AB|}$$

$$|AB|\tan 68° = 30$$

$$|AB| = \frac{30}{\tan 68°}$$

$$|AB| = 12·12 \text{ m}$$

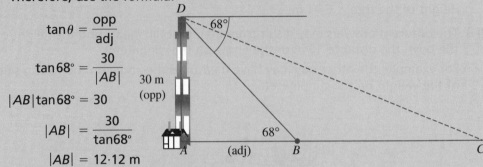

Therefore, |AB| = 12 m to the nearest metre.

(ii) To find |BC| we must first find |AC|:

Mark in the angle of depression 33°. This equals the angle of elevation from C to the top of the lighthouse. Label the sides in the large triangle, in relation to the 33° angle.

We have the opposite = 30 m and we want the adjacent side.

Therefore, use the formula:

$$\tan\theta = \frac{\text{opp}}{\text{adj}}$$

$$\tan 33° = \frac{30}{|AC|}$$

$$|AC|\tan 33° = 30$$

$$|AC| = \frac{30}{\tan 33°}$$

$$|AC| = 46·195 \text{ m}$$

Therefore, |AC| = 46 m to the nearest metre.

$$|AC| = |AB| + |BC| \quad \text{(Straight line)}$$
$$46 = 12 + |BC|$$
$$34 \text{ m} = |BC|$$

(iii) The boat travelled from B to C in ten seconds.

Distance = 34 m

Time = 10 s

$$\text{Speed} = \frac{\text{Distance}}{\text{Time}} = \frac{34}{10} = 3·4 \text{ m/s}$$

Two vertical poles A and B, each of height h, are standing on opposite sides of a level road. They are 24 m apart. The point P, on the road directly between the two poles, is a distance x from pole A. The angle of elevation from P to the top of pole A is 60°.

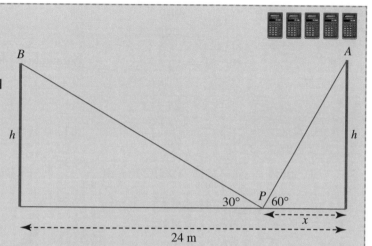

(i) Write h in terms of x.

(ii) From P, the angle of elevation to the top of pole B is 30°.

Find h, the height of the two poles. Give your answer in surd form.

Solution

(i) We want a relationship between h and x, therefore look at the smaller triangle.

Label the sides in relation to the 60° angle.

We want the opposite = h and the adjacent = x

Therefore, use the formula:

$$\tan\theta = \frac{\text{opp}}{\text{adj}}$$

$$\tan 60° = \frac{h}{x} \qquad \text{(substitute in known values)}$$

$$\sqrt{3} = \frac{h}{x}$$

$$x\sqrt{3} = h \qquad \text{(multiply both sides by } x)$$

(ii) In the larger triangle, the side on the bottom is equal to 24 m less the section x metres in length. Thus it is (24 − x) metres in length. Label the sides in relation to the 30° angle.

We have the adjacent = 24 − x menes and want the opposite.

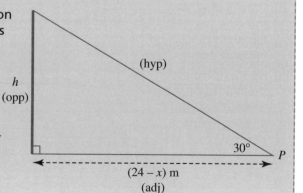

Therefore, use the formula:

$$\tan\theta = \frac{\text{opp}}{\text{adj}}$$

$$\tan 30° = \frac{h}{24 - x} \qquad \text{(substitute in known values)}$$

$$\frac{1}{\sqrt{3}} = \frac{h}{24 - x}$$

$$\frac{1}{\sqrt{3}} = \frac{x\sqrt{3}}{24 - x} \qquad \text{(let } h = x\sqrt{3}\text{)}$$

$$(\sqrt{3})(24 - x)\left(\frac{1}{\sqrt{3}}\right) = (\sqrt{3})(24 - x)\left(\frac{x\sqrt{3}}{24 - x}\right) \qquad \text{(multiply both sides by } \sqrt{3}(24 - x)\text{)}$$

$$(24 - x)(1) = \sqrt{3}(x\sqrt{3})$$

$$24 - x = x(3)$$

$$24 - x = 3x$$

$$24 = 4x$$

$$6 = x$$

$$h = x\sqrt{3}$$

Therefore, $h = 6\sqrt{3}$ m

The suggested time for this question was 10 minutes, which would suggest that the question would be worth 20 marks. However, the question was very poorly answered and consequently part (i) was awarded 5 marks and part (ii) was awarded 2 marks.

On a school trip to a monastic site, Clíodhna decided to measure the height of the round tower. She stood on a mound a horizontal distance of 30 m from the tower. Using a clinometer, Clíodhna measured the angle of elevation to the top of the tower to be 18° and the angle of depression to the bottom of the tower to be 32°.

(i) Draw a diagram showing Clíodhna's measurements.

(ii) Hence, calculate the height of the tower. Give your answer to one decimal place.

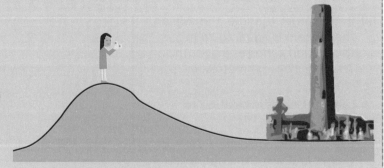

Solution

(i) Entering the measurements on the picture:

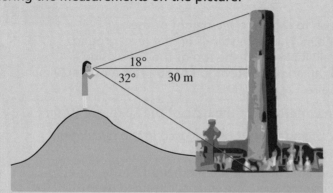

(ii) We can split the shape into two right-angled triangles:
Label the triangles ① and ②.

Label the sides of the triangles in
relation to the given angles.

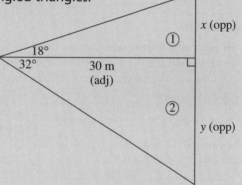

Triangle ①:

We have the adjacent = 30 m
and we want the opposite.
Therefore, use the formula:

$$\tan\theta = \frac{opp}{adj}$$

$$\tan 18° = \frac{x}{30}$$

$$30\tan 18° = x$$

$$9{\cdot}74759 \text{ m} = x$$

Triangle ②:

We have the adjacent = 30 m
and we want the opposite.
Therefore, use the formula:

$$\tan\theta = \frac{opp}{adj}$$

$$\tan 32° = \frac{y}{30}$$

$$30\tan 32° = y$$

$$18{\cdot}746 \text{ m} = y$$

Height of the tower = $x + y$

$$= 9{\cdot}74759 + 18{\cdot}746$$

$$= 28{\cdot}49359$$

Therefore, the height of the tower = 28·5 m, to one decimal place.

A group of students wish to calculate the height of the Millennium Spire in Dublin. The Spire stands on flat level ground. Maria, who is 1·72 m tall, looks up at the top of the Spire using a clinometer and records an angle of elevation of 60°. Her feet are 70 m from the base of the Spire.

Ultan measured the circumference of the base of the Spire as 7·07 m.

(i) Explain how Ultan's measurement will be used in the calculation of the height of the Spire.

(ii) Draw a suitable diagram and calculate the height of the Spire, to the nearest metre, using the measurements obtained by the students.

Solution

(i) The circumference can be used to calculate the radius of the base. This can then be added to the 70 m to find the exact distance Maria is from the centre of the base of the spire.

(ii) Diagram:

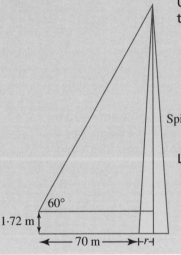

Use the circumference to find the radius of the base:

$$\text{Circumference} = 2\pi r$$
$$7 \cdot 07 = 2\pi r$$
$$\frac{7 \cdot 07}{2\pi} = r$$
$$1 \cdot 125 \text{ m} = r$$

Length of the base of the triangle $= 70 + 1 \cdot 125$
$$= 71 \cdot 125 \text{ m}$$

Label the sides in the triangle. We have the adjacent = 71·125 m and we want the opposite. Therefore, use the formula:

$$\tan\theta = \frac{opp}{adj}$$

$$\tan 60° = \frac{opp}{71\cdot 125}$$

71·125(tan 60°) = opp

123·19 m = opp

Height of Spire = 123·19 + height of Maria

Height of Spire = 123·19 + 1·72 = 124·91 m

Therefore, height of Spire = 125 m, to the nearest metre.

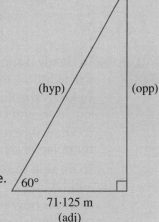

(hyp)   (opp)

60°

71·125 m
(adj)

exam focus

In a recent exam this question was very poorly answered. Consequently parts (i) and (ii) **together** were awarded a total of 5 marks. Make sure you spend no more than the suggested time on any question during the exam.

7 Perimeter, Area, Nets and Volume

☐ To clearly distinguish the difference between the units of measure,
e.g. length = m; area = m²; volume = m³

☐ To know the link between various units,
e.g. litres and cm³ [1l = 1,000 cm³]

☐ To know where to find the relevant information in the booklet of
formulae and tables

☐ To be able to recall formulae that are not in the booklet of formulae
and tables

☐ To know how to calculate the perimeter and areas of regular and
compound 2D shapes

☐ To know how to calculate the surface area and volumes of cylinders,
cones, cuboids, spheres, prisms and compound shapes

☐ To understand and be able to draw nets

☐ To gain the skills to apply the above knowledge to exam questions

Perimeter and area of 2D shapes with triangles and rectangles

The perimeter and area of squares and rectangles are sumarised below.

Square	Rectangle
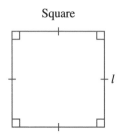	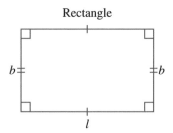

Perimeter $= l + l + l + l = 4l$

Area $= (l)(l) = l^2$

Perimeter $= l + b + l + b = 2(l + b)$

Area $= (l)(b) = lb$

You must know the formulae for the area of a rectangle square and the perimeter of a rectangle square as they are **not** in the booklet of formulae and tables.

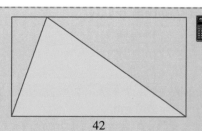

The diagram shows a rectangle of length 42 cm.

The area of the rectangle is 966 cm².

(i) Find the height of the rectangle.

(ii) Find the area of the shaded triangle.

Solution

(i) Equation given in disguise:

Note: the height of the rectangle is the same as the breadth

Area rectangle = length × breadth

$$966 = l \times b$$

$$966 = 42 \times b$$

$$23\,cm = b$$

(ii) Area of shaded triangle

$$\text{Area } \Delta = \frac{1}{2}(\text{base})(\text{perpendicular ht})$$

(see booklet of formulae and tables page 9)

$$\text{Area} = \frac{1}{2}(42)(23)$$

$$= \frac{1}{2}(966)$$

$$= 483\,cm^2$$

The rule for the perimeter of a triangle = the sum of the length of three sides. This must be known as it is **not** in the booklet of formulae and tables.

The area of a square is 49 cm². Find the length of the perimeter in millimetres.

Solution

Good reading skills are vital in this question.

- Square ⟹ All sides equal

- Perimeter ⟹ Add all four sides

- Millimetres ⟹ 1 cm = 10 mm. Always watch out for questions that combine different units of measure.

Let w = length of a side

Area of square = $(w)(w)$

$$49 = w^2$$
$$7 \text{ cm} = w$$

Perimeter = $7 + 7 + 7 + 7 = 28$ cm $= 28 \times 10$ mm
$$= 280 \text{ mm}$$

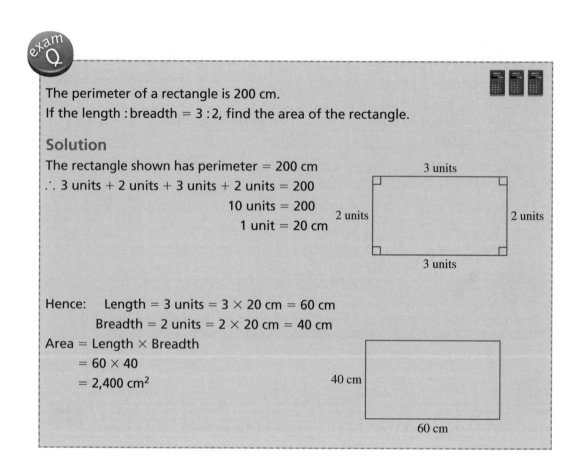

exam Q

The perimeter of a rectangle is 200 cm.
If the length : breadth = 3 : 2, find the area of the rectangle.

Solution

The rectangle shown has perimeter = 200 cm

∴ 3 units + 2 units + 3 units + 2 units = 200
$$10 \text{ units} = 200$$
$$1 \text{ unit} = 20 \text{ cm}$$

Hence: Length = 3 units = 3×20 cm = 60 cm

Breadth = 2 units = 2×20 cm = 40 cm

Area = Length × Breadth
$$= 60 \times 40$$
$$= 2,400 \text{ cm}^2$$

A box of tissues consists of 80 tissues each with dimensions 300 mm × 260 mm.

A roll of tissue consists of 120 tissues each with dimensions 24 cm × 22 cm.

Find in m² the total area of tissue:

(a) In the box **(b)** On the roll.

Hence, decide which is better value: 15 rolls of tissue for €22 or 16 boxes of tissue for €22.

Note: In this case, the area of tissue is concerned with **one** side of tissue only.

Solution

(a) Total area of tissue in the box = $(0.3 \times 0.26)\ 80 = 6.24\ m^2$

(b) Total area of tissue on the roll = $(0.24 \times 0.22)\ 120 = 6.336\ m^2$

It is easier to change units first than afterwards:

300 mm = 0·3 m	24 cm = 0·24 m
260 mm = 0·26 m	22 cm = 0·22 m

The word 'hence' in the question means that area is the criteria for value (and not, for example, the number of tissues).

Area of tissues in 16 boxes = $6.24 \times 16 = 99.84\ m^2$

Area of tissues on 15 rolls = $6.336 \times 15 = 95.04\ m^2$

$\therefore$ We state that 16 boxes of tissues are better value.

The question gave no consideration to the quality of tissue, whether the production method was ecofriendly or to individual preference of box versus roll. In this case, the only element considered was price. This may not be the case in other exam questions.

Perimeter and area of circles

Sinead measured the circumference (in red colour) of each of the following circles with a piece of thread. Her results are included in the table below.

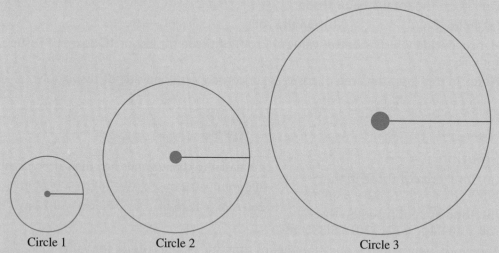

Circle 1   Circle 2   Circle 3

Using a ruler, measure the diameter of each circle and record your answers in the space provided.

Hence complete the table.

What do you notice?

	Circumference as measured by Sinead	Diameter	Circumference ÷ Diameter (1 decimal place)
Circle 1	6·3 cm		
Circle 2	13 cm		
Circle 3	18·5 cm		

Solution

Measuring each diameter with a ruler we find:

Circle 1   Has diameter 2 cm

Circle 2   Has diameter 4 cm

Circle 3   Has diameter 6 cm.

Fill in the table using a calculator to evaluate circumference ÷ diameter.

	Circumference as measured by Sinead	Diameter	Circumference ÷ Diameter (1 decimal place)
Circle 1	6·3 cm	2 cm	6·3 ÷ 2 = 3·15 ⟹ 3·2 cm
Circle 2	13 cm	4 cm	13·4 ÷ 4 = 3·25 ⟹ 3·3 cm
Circle 3	18·5 cm	6 cm	18·5 ÷ 6 = 3·08 ⟹ 3·1 cm

In each of the three circles, we see $\dfrac{\text{Circumference}}{\text{Diameter}}$ = A number close to π.

key point

- π is a ratio of the circumference of any circle to its diameter.
- $\pi = 3 \cdot 141592 \ldots$ is known nowadays to billions of decimal places.
- In the exam, you may be told to take π as a particular value, e.g $\frac{22}{7}$, $3 \cdot 14$.
- When using $\pi = \frac{22}{7}$, it is good practice to write the radius as a fraction, e.g $3 \cdot 5 = \frac{7}{2}$ or $18 = \frac{18}{1}$.
- If a question says to give your answer in terms of π, then leave π in the answer. Do not use $3 \cdot 14$ or $\frac{22}{7}$ for π.
- If you are not given an approximate value for π, then you must use the value given by the calculator.

exam Q

The rear windscreen wiper of a car rotates on an arm 40 cm long. The wiper blade is 25 cm long. The wiper rotates through an angle of 150°, as shown in the diagram.

Calculate the area of the windscreen cleaned by the wiper to the nearest cm².

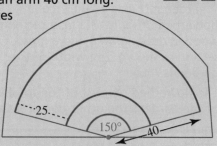

Solution

We use the formula for area of a sector:

$$= \pi r^2 \left(\frac{\theta}{360} \right) \qquad \text{(see booklet of formulae and tables page 9)}$$

on two sections of the windscreen.

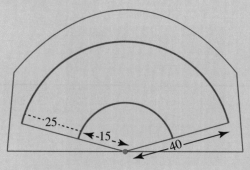

key point

The radius of the inner section is $40 - 25 = 15$ cm

Area of outer sector | Area of inner sector

$$= \pi(40)^2\left(\frac{150}{360}\right)$$

$$= \pi(15)^2\left(\frac{150}{360}\right)$$

$$= 2094{\cdot}395102 \text{ cm}^2$$

$$= 294{\cdot}5243113 \text{ cm}^2$$ (By calculator)

$$\therefore \text{ Area cleaned by the wiper} = 2094{\cdot}395102 - 294{\cdot}5243113$$

$$= 1799{\cdot}870791$$

$$= 1800 \text{ cm}^2$$ (To nearest cm²)

key point

When asked to round your answer, do not do any rounding until the last line in your work.

exam Q

A garden includes a semicircular flowerbed of radius 3·5 m, a rectangular wooden decking area and a grass section as shown. The width of the garden is 7 m.

The flowerbed covers $\frac{1}{5}$ of the total area of the garden. The other two areas are equal. Assume $\pi = \frac{22}{7}$.

Calculate:

(i) The area of the flowerbed

(ii) The area of the grass

(iii) y, the length of the garden

(iv) The exact amount of varnish required to paint the wooden decking when 1 litre covers 250,000 cm² of wood

(v) The length of the perimeter of the grass area.

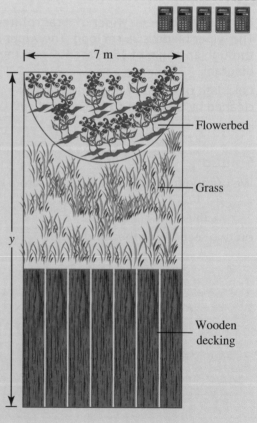

Solution

(i) The flowerbed is a semicircle.

The booklet of formulae and tables page 8 gives πr^2 as the area of a circle.

We need to halve it:

Area of flowerbed = Area of semicircle

$$A = \frac{1}{2}(\pi r^2)$$

$$= \frac{1}{2}\left(\frac{22}{7}\right)(3\cdot5)^2 \qquad \text{Radius} = \frac{1}{2}(7) = 3\cdot5$$

$$= 19\cdot25\,\text{m}^2$$

(ii) Area of entire garden = 5 × area of flowerbed = 5 × 19·25 = 96·25 m²

Area of grass = $\frac{2}{5}$(area of garden) = $\frac{2}{5}$(96·25) = 38·5 m²

(iii) Area of garden = length × breadth

$$A = y \times b$$

$$96\cdot25 = y \times 7$$

$$96\cdot25 = 7\,y$$

13·75 m = y (divide both sides by 7)

(iv) 1 litre covers 250,000 cm² $\Rightarrow$
1 litre covers 25 m²

Area of wooden decking
= Area of grass
= 38·5 m²

Number of litres required

$$= \frac{\text{Area to be covered}}{\text{Area covered by 1 litre}}$$

$$= \frac{38\cdot5}{25}$$

$$= 1\cdot54 \text{ litres}$$

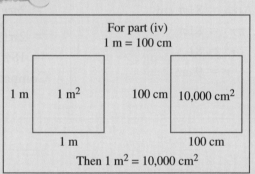

For part (iv)
1 m = 100 cm

1 m   1 m²

100 cm   10,000 cm²

1 m   100 cm

Then 1 m² = 10,000 cm²

(v) Let x = the length of the flowerbed
and grass section.

Area of flowerbed and grass

$$= 19\cdot25 + 38\cdot5$$

$$(7)(x) = 57\cdot75$$

$$7x = 57\cdot75$$

$$x = 8\cdot25 \text{ m}$$

Length of circumference of circle
= $2\pi r$ (see booklet of formulae and tables page 8)

Length of circumference of
semicircular portion of flowerbed

$$= \frac{1}{2}(2\pi r) = \frac{1}{2}(2)\left(\frac{22}{7}\right)(3\cdot5) = 11\,\text{m}$$

Perimeter of grass area = 8·25 + 7 + 8·25 + 11

$$= 34\cdot5 \text{ m}$$

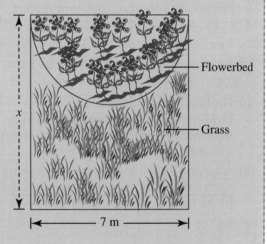

Flowerbed

Grass

x

7 m

Example

The area of a circle is 81π cm². Its length is $k\pi$ cm. Calculate k.

Solution

Equation given in disguise:

Area $= 81\pi$ cm²

$\therefore \pi r^2 = 81\pi$

$r^2 = 81$

$r = 9$ cm

Length (circumference) of a circle

$= 2\pi r$

$= 2\pi(9)$ (put in $r = 9$)

$= 18\pi$ cm

Comparing: $k\pi = 18\pi$

$k = 18$

Sally makes earrings from silver wire.

Her design includes two touching sectors of circles, as shown in the diagram.

The inner sector has centre Q, radius 1·4 cm.

The outer sector has centre B, radius 3 cm.

$|\angle ABC| = 60°$ and $|\angle PQR| = 108°$

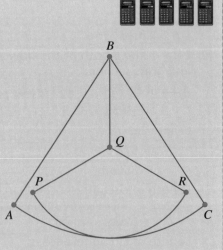

(i) Find the total length of silver wire required by Sally to make this earring. Give your answer correct to the nearest millimetre.

(ii) Allowing 10% for waste when making each earring, how many earrings will Sally make from a 1 m length of silver wire?

(iii) Hence, comment on how Sally could improve her manufacturing process.

Solution

(i) $|AB| = |CB| = 3$ and $|PQ| = |RQ| = 1\cdot4$ and $|BQ| = 3 - 1\cdot4 = 1\cdot6$

Length of arc $PR = \dfrac{108°}{360°}(2\pi r) = 0\cdot3\,(2\pi(1\cdot4)) = 2\cdot638937829$

Length of arc $AC = \dfrac{60°}{360°}(2\pi r) = \dfrac{1}{6}(2\pi(3)) = 3\cdot141592654$

Total length of silver wire in earring

$= |AB| + |CB| + |PQ| + |RQ| + |BQ| + \text{arc } PR + \text{arc } AC$

$= 3 + 3 + 1\cdot4 + 1\cdot4 + 1\cdot6 + 2\cdot6389 + 3\cdot1415$

$= 16\cdot1804$ cm

$= 162$ mm

(ii) 162 mm + 10% waste $= 162 + 16\cdot2 = 178\cdot2$ mm

1 m = 1,000 mm

$\therefore$ Sally can make $\dfrac{1{,}000}{178\cdot2} = 5\cdot61167\ldots$ five earrings from 1 m of silver wire.

(iii) If Sally could eliminate the 10% waste, she could make $\dfrac{1{,}000}{162} = 6\cdot17\ldots$ six earrings from 1 m of silver wire.

exam focus

In the exam, it is worth highlighting important words and units. When answering questions in the previous question, you could highlight touching sectors/inner and outer sector cm/millimetre/m.

Nets of 3D shapes

When a 3D shape is opened out, the flat shape is called the **net**.

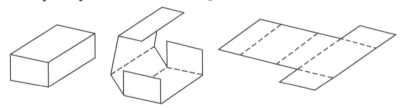

This is one possible **net** of a solid cube.

key point

There are 11 possible different nets of a cube.

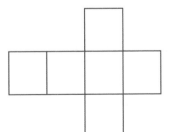

This is how it folds up to make the cube:

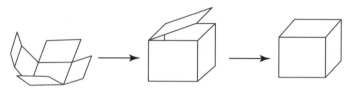

Example

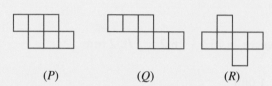

(P)　　　　　　　(Q)　　　　　　　(R)

(i) Which **one** of the three shapes above is **not** the net of a cube?

(ii) Given the side of each square is 1 cm, write down the perimeter of

(a) *P*　　　　　　(b) *Q*　　　　　　(c) *R*

Solution

(i) *P* is not the net of a cube.

(ii) (a) *P* has perimeter = 12 cm

(b) *Q* has perimeter = 14 cm

(c) *R* has perimeter = 14 cm

The net of a fair six-sided die is shown.

Write down:

(i) The probability of a score of 5

(ii) The probability of a score of 6.

			6
5	6	5	6
			6

Solution

(i) The probability of a score of

$$5 = \frac{2}{6} = \frac{1}{3}$$

(ii) The probability of a score of

$$6 = \frac{4}{6} = \frac{2}{3}$$

key point

A score of 5 is on two sides of the fair die.

A score of 6 is on four sides of the fair die.

The previous question combines nets and probability. We consistently see exam questions combining different topics from our course.

exam Q

The net for a figure with a square base is shown. Each grid unit represents 5 mm.

(a) Find *w*, the length of the base, and *d*, the height of each triangular side.

(b) Find the area of the base of the figure.

(c) Find the total surface area of the figure.

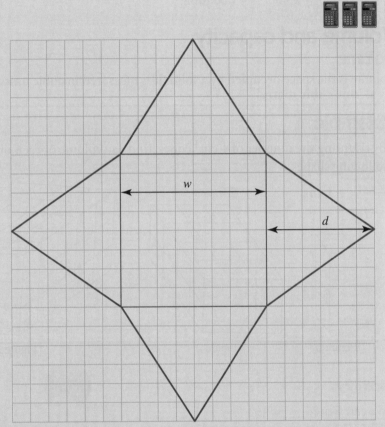

Drawing to scale can be very useful when dealing with a shape. In a scale of 1 to 20 every one unit on the diagram represents twenty units in real life. Scale may be examined in many different topics. This question incorporates scale with nets and area. It is vital that you develop the skill to work with scale wherever you meet it.

Solution

(a) $w = 8$ boxes $\times$ 5 mm = 40 mm

   $d = 6$ boxes $\times$ 5 mm = 30 mm

(b) Area of base = $w \times w = 40 \times 40 = 1{,}600$ mm^2

(c) Total surface area of the figure

   = Area of the square + 4(Area of one triangle)

   = $1{,}600 + 4\left(\frac{1}{2}\text{ Base} \times \text{perpendicular height}\right)$

   = $1{,}600 + 4\left(\frac{1}{2}\,40 \times 30\right)$

   = $1{,}600 + 2{,}400 = 4{,}000$ mm^2

> **key point**
>
> To find w and d simply count the number of (grid) boxes and multiply by 5 mm.

Volume and capacity

Volume

Volume is the space occupied by a solid. It is measured in cubic units, e.g. m^3, which we say as '**one cubic metre**'.

Example

By counting the number of 1 cm^3 cubes, find the volume of each of the following shapes.

 = 1 cm^3

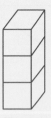

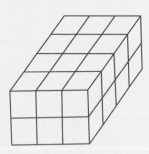

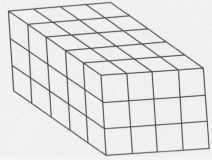

Figure 1   Figure 2   Figure 3

Solution

We can write:

Figure 1 has volume 3×1 cm^3 = 3 cm^3

Figure 2 has volume 24×1 cm^3 = 24 cm^3

Figure 3 has volume 60×1 cm^3 = 60 cm^3

> **key point**
>
> Figure 1 has $1 \times 1 \times 3 = 3$ cubes
>
> Figure 2 has $3 \times 4 \times 2 = 24$ cubes
>
> Figure 3 has $5 \times 4 \times 3 = 60$ cubes

Capacity

The capacity of a container is the amount of liquid it can hold.

The most commonly used measure is the litre.

> **key point**
>
> - 1 litre = 1,000 cm^3, i.e. a 1-litre bottle of water contains 1,000 cm^3 of liquid.
> - To convert litres to cubic centimetres (cm^3), multiply by 1,000.
> - 1 litre = 1,000 millilitres (ml) $\Rightarrow$ 1 cm^3 = 1 ml

Rectangular objects

1. Rectangular solid (cuboid)

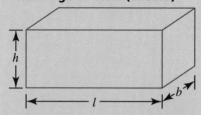

Volume = lbh

Surface area = $2lb + 2lh + 2bh$

2. Cube

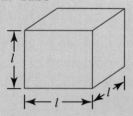

Volume = l^3

Surface area = $6l^2$

You must know the above formulae as they are **not** in the booklet of formulae and tables.

Example

The volume of a rectangular block is 560 cm^3.
If its length is 14 cm and its breadth is 8 cm, find
(i) its height and (ii) its surface area.

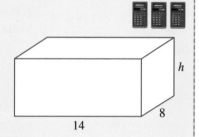

Solution

(i) Equation given in disguise:

$$\text{Volume} = 560 \text{ cm}^3$$
$$(14)(8)h = 560$$
$$112h = 560$$
$$h = \frac{560}{112} = 5 \text{ cm}$$

(ii) Surface area

$$= (\text{Front} + \text{Back}) + (\text{Top} + \text{Bottom})$$
$$\quad + (\text{Side} + \text{Side})$$
$$= 2(lh) + 2(lb) + 2(bh)$$
$$= 2(14)(5) + 2(14)(8) + 2(8)(5)$$
$$= 140 + 224 + 80$$
$$= 444 \text{ cm}^2$$

A jeweller buys a rectangular block of gold of
length 4 cm, width 3 cm and height 2 cm. 1 cm^3
of gold costs €400.

(i) Calculate the cost of the block of gold.

The jeweller needs 250 mm³ of gold to make a gold ring.

(ii) How many rings can be made from the block?

Each ring is sold for €120.

(iii) Calculate the amount of profit the jeweller makes on each ring.

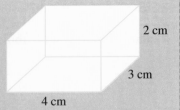

2 cm

3 cm

4 cm

Solution

(i) Volume block = 4 × 3 × 2 = 24 cm³

1 cm³ costs €400

⇒ 24 cm³ costs €400 × 24 = €9,600

(ii) ∴ 24 cm³ = 24,000 mm³

key point

1 cm² = 10 × 10 = 100 mm²

1 cm³ = 10 × 10 × 10 = 1,000 mm³

exam focus

Converting cm³ to mm³ posed a huge problem for candidates.

$$\text{Number of rings} = \frac{\text{Total volume available}}{\text{Volume of one ring}} = \frac{24,000}{250} = 96 \text{ rings}$$

(iii) Total cost = €9,600

Total rings = 96

$$\therefore \text{Cost of one ring} = \frac{\text{Total cost}}{\text{Number of rings}}$$

$$= \frac{9,600}{96} = €100$$

Profit = Selling price − Cost price

$$= €120 − €100$$

$$= €20 \text{ profit on each ring}$$

exam Q

The net for a box, with a square base, is shown below.

The shaded areas are flaps of width 1 cm which are needed to assemble the box.

The height of the box is h cm and the length and breadth are x cm as shown on the diagram.

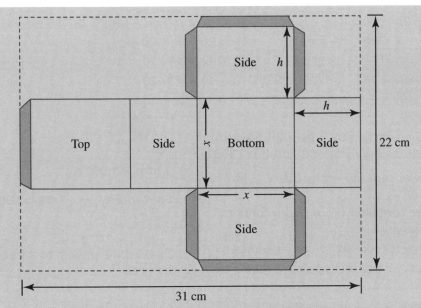

(i) From the diagram, write down an expression in x and h equal to

    (a) 30   **(b)** 20

(ii) Solve the equations found in (i) to find the value of h and the value of x.

(iii) Calculate the capacity of the box in litres.

(iv) Comment on the statement:

    'This box is too small to serve as a container for ice cream in a shop fridge.'

(i) (a) From the diagram $\Rightarrow$ 1 + x + h + x + h = 31

$$2x + 2h = 30$$

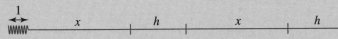

(b)

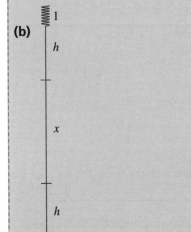

$$\therefore 1 + h + x + h + 1 = 22$$
$$2h + x = 20$$

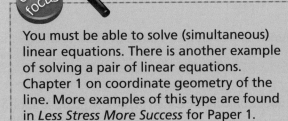

You must be able to solve (simultaneous) linear equations. There is another example of solving a pair of linear equations. Chapter 1 on coordinate geometry of the line. More examples of this type are found in *Less Stress More Success* for Paper 1.

(ii) 2x + 2h = 30   ①   put h = 5   into ① or ②

2h + x = 20   ②   2h + x = 20   ②

−x − h = −15   ① ÷ by −2   2(5) + x = 20

x + 2h = 20   ② Rearranged   10 + x = 20

h = 5   (Add)   x = 10

(iii) Volume of the box = (length)(breadth)(height) = $(x)(x)(h)$ = (10)(10)(5) = 500 cm³

Answer capacity of the box = $\frac{1}{2}$ litre

key point

1 litre = 1,000 cm³

For capacity ⟹ $\frac{1}{2}$ litre = 500 cm³

(iv) $\frac{1}{2}$ litre container of ice cream contains 3/6 servings.

⟹ Box far too big for an individual

⟹ Box just correct size for a family treat

} Choose one answer, to agree or disagree

Uniform cross-section

Many solid objects have the same cross-section throughout their length. Here are some examples.

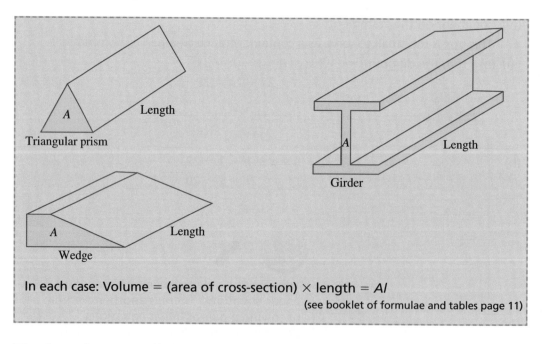

Triangular prism — A, Length

Wedge — A, Length

Girder — A, Length

In each case: Volume = (area of cross-section) × length = Al

(see booklet of formulae and tables page 11)

The above objects are called prisms. A prism is a solid object which has the same cross-section throughout its length and its sides are parallelograms.

A solid cylinder has a uniform cross-section, but it is not a prism.

So to find the volume of a solid object with a uniform cross-section, find the area of the cross-section and multiply this by its length.

Example

This triangular prism has a
volume of 513 cm³. Work out
the length of the base of its
cross-section.

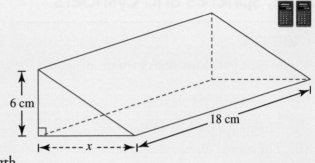

6 cm

18 cm

x

Solution

The volume of a prism
= (area of cross-section) × length

An equation given in disguise:

$$\text{Volume} = 513$$
$$(\text{Area of triangle}) \, l = 513$$
$$\frac{1}{2}(x)(6)(18) = 513$$
$$54x = 513 \qquad (\text{divide both sides by 54})$$
$$x = 9 \cdot 5 \, \text{cm}$$

Example

This prism is 8 cm long.
The ends are equilateral triangles
with sides of 4 cm.
Draw an accurate net of the prism.
Note: diagram **not** to scale.

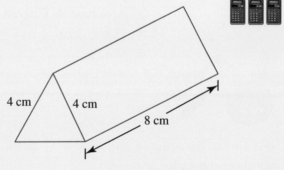

4 cm   4 cm

8 cm

Solution

Step 1: Draw the rectangular faces of the
prism. Each rectangle is 8 cm long
and 4 cm wide.

Step 2: The ends of the prism are
equilateral triangles.
The length of each side of the
triangles is 4 cm.
Use your compass to construct the
equilateral triangles.

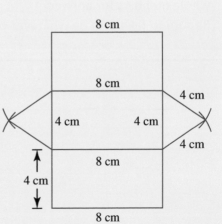

8 cm

8 cm

4 cm

4 cm   4 cm

4 cm

4 cm

8 cm

8 cm

Cone, spheres and cylinders

Example

A solid cone has dimensions as in the diagram.

Take $\pi = \dfrac{22}{7}$ and calculate:

$l = 10$ cm

(i) The area of the base of the cone

(ii) The curved surface area of the cone

(iii) The total surface area of the cone.

$r = 7$ cm

Solution

(i) Area base = Area circle

$$= \pi r^2 \qquad \text{(from booklet of formulae and tables page 8)}$$

$$= \frac{22}{7}(7)^2$$

$$= 154 \text{ cm}^2$$

(ii) Curved surface area = $\pi r l$ (from booklet of formulae and tables page 10)

$$= \left(\frac{22}{7}\right)(7)(10)$$

$$= 220 \text{ cm}^2$$

(iii) Total surface area = part (i) + part (ii)

$$= \text{Area base} + \text{Curved surface area}$$

$$= 154 + 220$$

$$= 374 \text{ cm}^2$$

exam focus

It is vital to do as asked and let $\pi = \dfrac{22}{7}$ in this question. As a result, we get whole numbers for answers.

Be sure to take π to be whatever you are told in the question.

(i) A golf ball has radius 1·5 cm.

Find its volume in terms of π.

(ii) Four such golf balls, placed one on top of the other fit exactly into a cylindrical tube. Find:

(a) The radius of the tube

(b) The height of the tube

(c) The volume of the tube, in terms of π.

(iii) What fraction of the internal volume is not occupied by the golf balls?

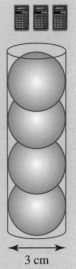

3 cm

Solution

(i) Volume of golf ball = Volume of sphere

(from booklet of formulae and tables page 10)

$$= \frac{4}{3}\pi r^3$$

$$= \frac{4}{3}\pi(1 \cdot 5)^3 = \frac{4}{3}\pi(3 \cdot 375) = \frac{9}{2}\pi \text{ cm}^3$$

(ii) (a) Radius of cylindrical tube = 1·5 cm (the same as the ball)

(b) Height of cylindrical tube = 4 (diameter ball) = 4(3) = 12 cm

(c) Volume of cylindrical tube = $\pi r^2 h$

$$= \pi(1 \cdot 5)^2 \, 12$$

$$= 27\pi \text{ cm}^3$$

(iii) Volume of four golf balls = $4\left(\frac{9}{2}\pi\right) = 18\pi \text{ cm}^3$

Volume not occupied = $27\pi - 18\pi = 9\pi \text{ cm}^3$

Fraction not occupied by the four golf balls $= \dfrac{9\pi}{27\pi} = \dfrac{9}{27} = \dfrac{1}{3}.$

The dimensions of two solid cylinders are shown in the diagrams below.

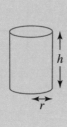

h

r

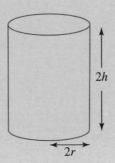

$2h$

$2r$

(a) Calculate the ratio of the curved surface area of the smaller cylinder to the curved surface area of the larger cylinder.

(b) Calculate the ratio of the volume of the smaller cylinder to the volume of the larger cylinder.

key point

Solution

(a) $\dfrac{\text{Curved surface of small cylinder}}{\text{Curved surface of large cylinder}} = \dfrac{2\pi(r)(h)}{2\pi(2r)(2h)} = \dfrac{2}{8} = \dfrac{1}{4}$

Use curved surface formula on both cylinders.

(See booklet of formulae and tables page 10)

key point

(b) $\dfrac{\text{Volume of small cylinder}}{\text{Volume of big cylinder}} = \dfrac{\pi(r)^2(h)}{\pi(2r)^2(2h)} = \dfrac{\pi r^2 h}{\pi 4 r^2 2h} = \dfrac{1}{8}$

Use the volume formula on both cylinders.

---

exam Q

The height and radius of a cone are equal. The slant height, l, is $\sqrt{98}$ cm. Find the volume of the cone in terms of π.

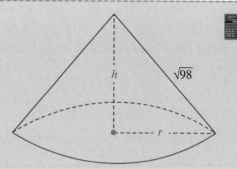

Solution

Since $h = r$ we can let $x = h$ and $x = r$.

The theorem of Pythagoras $\Rightarrow (\text{hyp})^2 = (\text{opp})^2 + (\text{adj})^2$

$$(\sqrt{98})^2 = x^2 + x^2$$
$$98 = 2x^2$$
$$49 = x^2$$
$$7 = x$$

Hence, $h = 7$ cm and $r = 7$ cm.

Volume of cone $= \dfrac{1}{3}\pi r^2 h$

$= \dfrac{1}{3}\pi(7)^2(7)$

$= \dfrac{1}{3}\pi(49)(7)$

$= \dfrac{343\pi}{3}$ cm^3

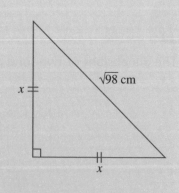

(i) Which of the following, diagram P or diagram Q, is the net of a cylinder? Justify your choice.

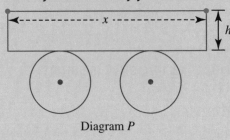

Diagram P

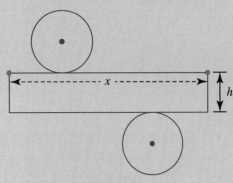

Diagram Q

(ii) Given that the identical circles have a diameter of 20 m, write down the radius of the circles.

(iii) If the volume of the cylinder is 2,512 m³, using volume $= \pi r^2 h$, solve for h. Assume $\pi = 3\cdot14$.

(iv) Calculate x, the length of the rectangle.

(v) The cylinder is used as a military bunker. For security reasons, the entire cylinder is to be covered by a copper mesh at a cost of €295 per square metre. Find the cost of the copper required to the nearest €1,000.

Solution

(i) Diagram Q is the net of a cylinder.

Diagram P is not the net of a cylinder because both circles are on the bottom.

(ii) Diameter $= 2r = 20$ m $\therefore r = 10$ m

(iii) $\pi r^2 h = 2{,}512$

$3\cdot14(10)^2 h = 2{,}512$

$314 h = 2{,}512$

$h = 8$ m

(iv) Since Q is the net of a cylinder, then x, the length of the rectangle, equals the circumference of the circle.

$$\therefore x = 2\pi r$$
$$x = 2(3{\cdot}14)(10)$$
$$x = 62{\cdot}8 \text{ m}$$

(v) Total surface area of cylinder =

$$= \pi r^2 + \pi r^2 + xh$$
$$= (3{\cdot}14)(10)^2 + (3{\cdot}14)(10)^2 + (62{\cdot}8)(8)$$
$$= 314 + 314 + 502{\cdot}4$$
$$= 1{,}130{\cdot}4 \text{ m}^2$$

The total cost = $1{,}130{\cdot}4 \times 295 = 333{,}468$
$$= €333{,}000$$

exam focus

Using the net of the cylinder makes the solution to **(v)** above very simple.

Compound volumes

You may be asked to find the volume of an object which is made up of different shapes. **When this happens, use the following steps:**

1. Split the solid up into regular shapes, for which we have formulae to calculate the volume or surface area.
2. Add these results together.

A solid metal ornament consists of a hemisphere of radius length 4 cm surmounted by a solid cone.

(i) Find, in terms of π, the volume of the hemisphere.

(ii) The cone's volume is twice the hemisphere's. Find h, the height of the cone.

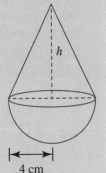

4 cm

Solution

(i) The volume of a sphere $= \dfrac{4}{3}\pi r^3$

The volume of a hemisphere $= \dfrac{1}{2}\left[\dfrac{4}{3}\pi r^3\right] = \dfrac{2}{3}\pi r^3$

$$= \dfrac{2}{3}\pi (4)^3$$

$$= \dfrac{2}{3}\pi (64)$$

$$= \dfrac{128}{3}\pi \text{ cm}^3$$

Part **(i)** asks for the answer *in terms of π*. This is a hint for **(ii)**.

(ii) Reading the words tells us that the volume of cone = twice volume of hemisphere.

In pictures: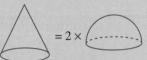

In mathematics: $\dfrac{1}{3}\pi r^2 h = 2\left[\dfrac{128}{3}\pi\right]$

$\dfrac{1}{3}r^2 h = 2\left[\dfrac{128}{3}\right]$ (divide both sides by π)

$r^2 h = 2[128]$ (multiply both sides by 3)

$(4)^2 h = 2[128]$ (substitute 4 for r)

$16h = 256$

$h = 16$ cm

(i) A container is in the shape of a cylinder on top of a hemisphere as shown.

The cylinder has a radius of 6 cm and the container has a height of 20 cm.

Calculate the volume of the container in terms of π.

(ii) One-third of the volume of the container is filled with water.

Calculate, d, the depth of the water in the container.

Solution

(i) Volume container = Volume cylinder + Volume $\frac{1}{2}$ sphere

$$= \pi r^2 h + \frac{1}{2}\left(\frac{4}{3}\pi r^3\right)$$

$$= \pi(6)^2(14) + \frac{2}{3}\pi(6)^3$$

$$= 504\pi + 144\pi = 648\pi \text{ cm}^3$$

Height cylinder = $20 - 6 = 14$

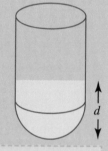

(ii) The empty section is a cylinder height h.

$$\therefore \pi r^2 h = 432\pi$$
$$(6)^2 h = 432$$
$$36h = 432$$
$$h = 12 \text{ cm}$$

From above diagram:
$$d + h = 20$$
$$d + 12 = 20$$
$$d = 8 \text{ cm}$$

$\frac{1}{3}$ of container full

$\Rightarrow \frac{2}{3}$ of container empty.

$\frac{2}{3}$ Volume container = $\frac{2}{3}[648\pi] = 432\pi$

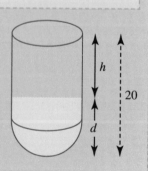

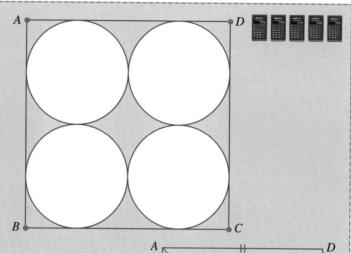

Four identical spheres fit exactly into a cuboid, the plan of which is shown in the diagram. Given that $|AC| = 6\sqrt{2}$ cm, find:

(i) The radius of a sphere

(ii) The volume of the space in the cuboid not occupied by the spheres, correct to the nearest integer.

Solution

(i) Let x = length of each side of square

From Pythagoras, we write:

$$|AC|^2 = |AB|^2 + |BC|^2$$
$$(6\sqrt{2})^2 = x^2 + x^2$$
$$72 = 2x^2$$
$$36 = x^2 \implies 6 \text{ cm} = x$$

From diagram: $4r = 6$.

$\therefore$ Radius $= r = \dfrac{6}{4} = \dfrac{3}{2}$ cm

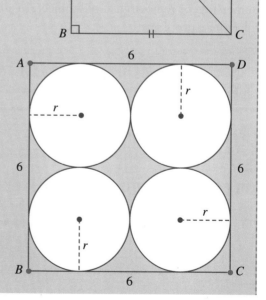

(ii) Volume of cuboid $= l \times b \times h$

$$= 6 \times 6 \times 2r$$

$$= 6 \times 6 \times 2\left(\frac{3}{2}\right)$$

$$= 108 \text{ cm}^3$$

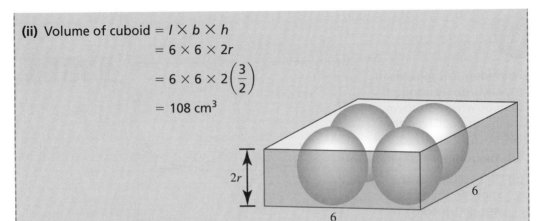

Volume of 4 spheres $= 4\left(\frac{4}{3}\pi r^3\right)$

$$= \frac{16}{3}\pi\left(\frac{3}{2}\right)^3 = \frac{16}{3}\pi\left(\frac{27}{8}\right) = 18\pi \text{ cm}^3$$

Volume of cuboid not occupied by spheres $= 108 - 18\pi = 51 \text{ cm}^3$

Displaced liquid

In many questions, we have to deal with situations where liquid is displaced by immersing, or removing, a solid object. In all cases, the following principle helps us to solve these problems:

> Volume of displaced liquid = Volume of immersed solid object

(i) Find the volume of a solid sphere with a diameter of length 3 cm. Give your answer in terms of π.

(ii) A cylindrical vessel with internal diameter of length 15 cm contains water. The surface of the water is 11 cm from the top of the vessel.

How many solid spheres, each with diameter of length 3 cm, must be placed in the vessel in order to bring the surface of the water to 1 cm from the top of the vessel? Assume that all the spheres are submerged in the water.

Solution

(i) Diameter = 3, which means radius = $\dfrac{3}{2}$.

Volume of sphere $= \dfrac{4}{3}\pi r^3 = \dfrac{4}{3}\pi\left(\dfrac{3}{2}\right)^3 = \dfrac{4}{3}\pi\left(\dfrac{27}{8}\right) = \pi\left(\dfrac{9}{2}\right)$ cm^3

(ii) Diameter = 15, which means radius = $\dfrac{15}{2}$.

Note: The height of the red cylinder = 11 − 1 = 10 cm.

Volume of the red cylinder $= \pi r^2 h$

$= \pi\left(\dfrac{15}{2}\right)^2(10) = \pi\left(\dfrac{225}{4}\right)(10) = \pi\,\dfrac{1{,}125}{2}$ cm^3

How many spheres are required to equal this red cylinder in volume?

The number of spheres required $= \dfrac{\text{Volume of red cylinder}}{\text{Volume of one sphere}}$

$= \dfrac{\pi\,\frac{1{,}125}{2}}{\pi\,\frac{9}{2}} = \left(\dfrac{1{,}125}{2}\right)\left(\dfrac{2}{9}\right) = 125$ spheres

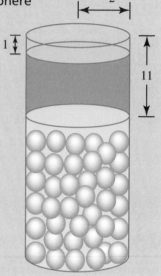

$r = \dfrac{15}{2}$

1

11

Recasting

Many of the questions we meet require us to solve a recasting problem. In these questions, a certain solid object is melted down and its shape is changed. We use the following fact:

> The volume of the object remains the same after it is melted down unless we are told otherwise in the question.

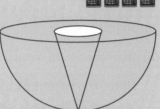

A solid metal hemisphere has a radius of 12 cm.

(a) Calculate the volume of the hemisphere. Give your answer in terms of π.

(b) A solid cone of radius 4 cm and height 12 cm is cut from the hemisphere. Calculate the volume of the cone. Give your answer in terms of π.

(c) The remaining metal in the hemisphere is melted down and recast into cones of the same dimensions as the cone above. How many cones can be formed from the remaining metal?

Solution

(a) Volume hemisphere $= \dfrac{1}{2}\left[\dfrac{4}{3}\pi r^3\right] = \dfrac{2}{3}\pi(12)^3 = 1{,}152\,\pi$ cm^3

(b) Volume cone $= \dfrac{1}{3}\pi r^2 h = \dfrac{1}{3}\pi(4)^2(12) = 64\pi$ cm^3

(c) Volume remaining metal = Volume hemisphere − Volume cone

$\qquad\qquad\qquad\qquad = 1{,}152\,\pi - 64\,\pi = 1{,}088\,\pi$

$\qquad$ Number of cones formed $= \dfrac{\text{Volume remaining metal}}{\text{Volume cone}}$

$\qquad\qquad\qquad\qquad\qquad = \dfrac{1{,}088\,\pi}{64\,\pi}$

$\qquad\qquad\qquad\qquad\qquad = 17.$

Moving liquids

In many questions, we have to deal with moving liquid from one container to another container of different dimensions or shape. Again, to help us solve the problem we use the fact that:

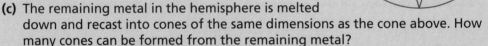

The volume of the moved liquid does not change unless we are told otherwise in the question.

(a) A container in the shape of a cylinder has a capacity of 50 litres. The height of the cylinder is 0·7 m. Find the length of the diameter of the cylinder. Give your answer correct to the nearest whole number.

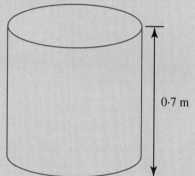

0·7 m

Solution

Convert all units to cm.

Then 1 litre = 1,000 cm³

and 50 litres = 50,000 cm³

$$h = 0·7 \text{ m} = 70 \text{ cm}$$

Volume of cylinder = 50 l = 50,000 cm³

$$\pi \, r^2 h = 50,000$$

$$\pi \, r^2 (70) = 50,000$$

$$r^2 = \frac{50,000}{\pi(70)} = 227·3642$$

$$r = 15·0786$$

Answer r = 15 cm correct to the nearest whole number

(b) A rectangular tank has a length of 0·6 m, a width of 0·35 m and its height measures 15 cm. Find the capacity of the rectangular tank.

Solution

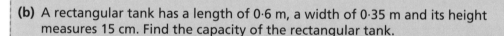

Length = 0·6 m = 60 cm

Width = 0·35 m = 35 cm

Height = 15 cm

Volume of rectangular tank = 60 × 35 × 15 = 31,500 cm³

We know 31,500 cm³ = $\frac{31,500}{1,000}$ = 31·5 litres

(c) The rectangular tank is full of water. This water is then poured into the cylindrical container in (a) above. Find the depth of water in the cylinder. Give your answer correct to one decimal place.

Solution

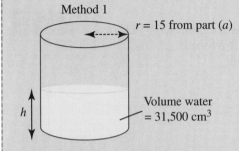

Method 1

$r = 15$ from part (a)

h

Volume water
$= 31{,}500 \text{ cm}^3$

Volume cylinder water $= \pi r^2 h$

$$31{,}500 = \pi(15)^2\, h$$

$$31{,}500 = \pi(225)\, h$$

$$\frac{31{,}500}{\pi(225)} = h$$

$$44{\cdot}56338 = h$$

Answer $h = 44{\cdot}6$ cm correct to one decimal place

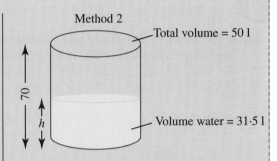

Method 2

Total volume $= 50\,\text{l}$

70

h

Volume water $= 31{\cdot}5\,\text{l}$

$$\frac{\text{Volume water}}{\text{Volume cylinder}} = \frac{\text{Height of water}}{\text{Height of cylinder}}$$

$$\frac{31{\cdot}5}{50} = \frac{h}{70}$$

$$\frac{31{\cdot}5 \times 70}{50} = h$$

$$44{\cdot}1 \text{ cm} = h$$

key point

Both answers for h are not equal because the radius in part (a) $r = 15{\cdot}0786$ cm is replaced by an approximate value $r = 15$ cm.

exam focus

The suggested maximum time was 10 minutes for this question, which was worth a total of 17 marks.

These marks were awarded as follows:

- part (a) was awarded 10 marks
- part (b) was awarded 5 marks
- part (c) was awarded 2 marks.

It is vital that you do not exceed the maximum time suggested for a question.

Pay good attention to detail at the start of the question. Avoid making basic slips and blunders and you will do very well.

Water is flowing through a cylindrical pipe at a speed of 35 cm/sec.
The radius of the pipe is 5 cm.

The water pours into a cubic tank of side 1 m. Find,
correct to the nearest whole number, the rise in the
depth of the water in the tank in 5 minutes.

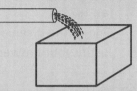

Solution

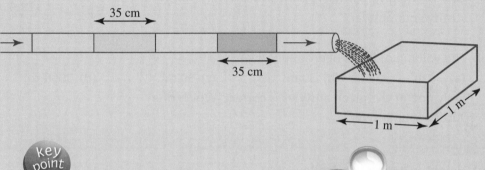

key point

Each cylindrical section is the amount of
water that flows into the tank every second.
It is vital that you understand this concept,
to answer this question correctly.

exam focus

5 min = 300 secs
1 m = 100 cm.

Volume of water delivered per second $= \pi r^2 h$

$\qquad\qquad = \pi(5)^2(35) = 2748{\cdot}893572$ cm³

∴ Volume of water delivered in 300 seconds $= (2748{\cdot}893572)300$

$\qquad\qquad\qquad\qquad = 824{,}668{\cdot}0716$ cm³

Let $w =$ Increase in depth of water in
the tank

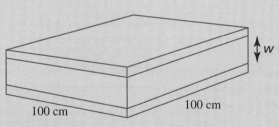

exam focus

This is a classic example of
a question that combines
different units of measure.

Now $(100)(100)(w) = 824{,}668{\cdot}0716$

$\qquad\qquad w = 82$ cm

(i) John's height is given as:

(a) 167 cm   (b) 1·67 m   (c) 16·7 litre   (d) 1,670 mm

One of the given answers is **incorrect**. Which one?

Justify your answer.

(ii) Ray has a field with an area of:

(a) 14·3 hectares   (b) 1,430 m^3 (c) 143,000 m^2

One of the given answers is **incorrect**. Which one?

Justify your answer.

(iii) The volume of Erin's bedroom is given as:

(a) 30 m   (b) 30 m^2 (c) 30 m^3 (d) 3000 cm^3

Only one of the given answers is **correct**. Which one?

Justify your answer.

Solution

(i) Height in mm; cm; m is allowed

Height in *l* litres is **not** allowed   **(c)** Incorrect

(ii) Area in hectares or m^2 is allowed

Area in m^3 is **not** allowed   **(b)** Incorrect

(iii) Volume in m^3 or cm^3 is allowed

3000 cm^3 is far too small, it's the
size of a shoe box!   **(c)** Correct

 aims
☐ To be able to list and calculate the number of outcomes of a situation
☐ To understand the two fundamental principles of counting

Outcomes

The result of an operation is called an **outcome**. For example, if we throw a die, one possible outcome is 2. If we throw a die, there are six possible outcomes: 1, 2, 3, 4, 5 or 6.

Fundamental principle of counting 1

Suppose one operation has m possible outcomes and that a second operation has n outcomes. The number of possible outcomes when performing the first operation **followed by** the second operation is $m \times n$.

Performing one operation **and** another operation means we **multiply** the number of possible outcomes.

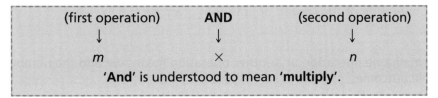

(first operation)	**AND**	(second operation)
↓	↓	↓
m	×	n

'And' is understood to mean 'multiply'.

Note: We assume that the outcome of one operation does not affect the number of possible outcomes of the other operation.

The fundamental principle of counting 1 can be extended to three or more operations.

Example

Sharon wants to buy a dress. The dress is available as follows:

Size	Small	Medium	Large
Colour	Blue	Red	

(i) How many possible outcomes are there for Sharon's purchase?
(ii) List these outcomes.

Solution

(i) Total number of outcomes = (number of sizes) AND (number of colours)

Total number of outcomes = $(3) \times (2)$

Total number of outcomes = 6

(ii) The 6 possible outcomes are:

Small and Blue   Medium and Blue   Large and Blue

Small and Red   Medium and Red   Large and Red

There are very few calculations involved with some of these questions. This means it is very important that you show the method you used to solve the problem. **In general, the answer alone, with no workings, may not be awarded full marks.**

Fundamental principle of counting 2

Suppose one operation has *m* possible outcomes and that a second operation has *n* outcomes. Then the number of possible outcomes of the first operation or the second operation is given by *m* + *n*.

Performing one operation **or** another operation means we **add** the number of possible outcomes.

(first operation)	OR	(second operation)
↓	↓	↓
m	+	*n*

'**Or**' is understood to mean '**add**'.

Note: We assume it is not possible for both operations to occur. In other words, there is no overlap of the two operations.

The fundamental principle 2 can be extended to three or more operations, as long as none of the operations overlap.

- '**And**' is understood to mean '**multiply**'.

- '**Or**' is understood to mean '**add**'.

Example

Ciara goes to the shop to buy herself a snack. She plans to buy either a chocolate bar or a bag of crisps. The shop has 4 different types of chocolate bar. The shop has 5 different types of bags of crisps.

How many possible outcomes are there for the snack that Ciara buys?

Solution

Total number of outcomes = (no. of chocolate bars) OR (no. of bags of crisps)

Total number of outcomes = (4) + (5)

Total number of outcomes = 9

A restaurant offers an early bird menu, which has 3 starters, 5 main courses, 4 desserts and an option of tea or coffee. How many different ways can you order a four course meal?

Solution

Total number of ways = (starters) AND (main courses) AND (desserts) AND (drinks)

Total number of ways = (3) × (5) × (4) × (2)

Total number of ways = 120

Colin prints his holiday photographs in a camera shop. The shop can print photographs in sizes small, medium or large, colour or black and white, glossy or matt finish.

  (i) How many different ways are there for Colin to print a photograph?

  (ii) Colin wants to print all his photos in medium size. How many ways are there for him to print his photos now?

Solution

  (i) Total number of ways = (size) AND (colour) AND (finish)

   Total number of ways = (3) × (2) × (2)

   Total number of ways = 12

  (ii) Since Colin wants all his photos to be in medium size, then there is only one option for the size.

   Total number of ways = (size) AND (colour) AND (finish)

   Total number of ways = (1) × (2) × (2)

   Total number of ways = 4

> **key point**
>
> In this question 'black and white' counts as only one option.

John is going to a festival for the weekend. Each outfit he will wear consists of a pair of jeans, a shirt, a jumper and a pair of shoes. He has packed:

     3 pairs of jeans (black, navy and blue)

     4 shirts (white, green, yellow and red)

     2 jumpers (black and brown)

     3 pairs of shoes (boots, sandals and flip-flops)

(i) Write down two examples of different outfits John could wear.

(ii) How many different possible outfits can John wear over the weekend?

Solution

(i) Example 1: Black jeans, green shirt, brown jumper and sandals

Example 2: Blue jeans, red shirt, black jumper and boots

(ii) Total number of outfits = (jeans) AND (shirts) AND (jumpers) AND (shoes)

$$= (3) \times (4) \times (2) \times (3)$$

$$= 72$$

Therefore, there are 72 different outfits John can wear.

A restaurant advertises its lunch menus using the sign below:

3-course lunch for €15

Choose from our range of

starters, main courses and desserts

180 different lunches to choose from!

(i) The menu has a choice of five starters and nine main courses. How many items must appear on the dessert menu to justify the above claim of 180 different lunches?

(ii) On a particular day, one of the starters and one of the main courses is not available. How many different three-course lunches is it possible to have on that day?

Solution

(i) Total number of lunches = (starters) AND (main courses) AND (desserts)

$$180 = (5) \times (9) \times \text{(number of desserts)}$$
$$180 = 45 \times \text{(number of desserts)}$$
$$4 = \text{number of desserts}$$

(ii) There will now be four starters and eight main courses and four desserts.

Total number of lunches = (starters) AND (main courses) AND (desserts)

$$= (4) \times (8) \times (4)$$
$$= 128$$

Therefore, there are 128 different three-course lunches possible on that day.

A football strip consists of a shirt, shorts and socks.

Aspen United has two shirts, blue and green, from which to select. They can also select from three different colours of shorts and five different colours of socks, including red in each case.

(i) Calculate how many different strips Aspen United can have.

(ii) Willow Celtic plays in an all-red strip. When Aspen United plays Willow Celtic, Aspen United are not allowed to use their red shorts or their red socks. Calculate how many different strips Aspen United can have when they play Willow Celtic.

Solution

(i) Total number of strips = (shirt) AND (shorts) AND (socks)

$$= (2) \times (3) \times (5)$$
$$= 30$$

Therefore, Aspen United can have 30 different strips.

(ii) If Aspen United cannot wear their red shorts or socks, then they have 2 shorts to pick from and 4 colours of socks.

Total number of strips = (shirt) AND (shorts) AND (socks)

$$= (2) \times (2) \times (4)$$
$$= 16$$

Therefore, when Aspen United play Willow Celtic, they can have 16 different strips.

Sample space

A sample space is the set of all possible outcomes. A sample space can be very useful for seeing all possible outcomes and working out any appropriate probabilities.

A sample space can be represented as a list of outcomes, a two-way table or a tree diagram. These three methods are shown in the next example.

key point

All possible outcomes can be shown using either a list, a two-way table or a tree diagram.

Example

A game consists of spinning a five-sided spinner, labelled P, Q, R, S and T, and tossing a coin.

An outcome is a letter and a head or a tail.

(i) How many outcomes of the game are possible?

(ii) List all the possible outcomes of the game.

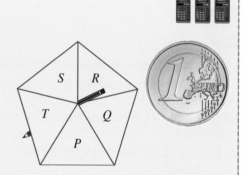

Solution

(i) Total number of outcome = (outcomes on spinner) AND (outcomes on coin)
$$= (5) \times (2)$$
$$= 10$$

(ii) There are three methods we can use to list the outcomes:

Method 1:

List of outcomes:

$(P, H), (Q, H), (R, H), (S, H), (T, H)$
$(P, T), (Q, T), (R, T), (S, T), (T, T)$

Method 2:

Using a two-way table (sample space):

		Spinner				
		P	Q	R	S	T
Coin	Head	•	•	•	•	•
	Tail	•	•	•	•	•

A dot indicates an outcome.
There are 10 dots (5 × 2).

Method 3:

Tree diagram:

Outcomes

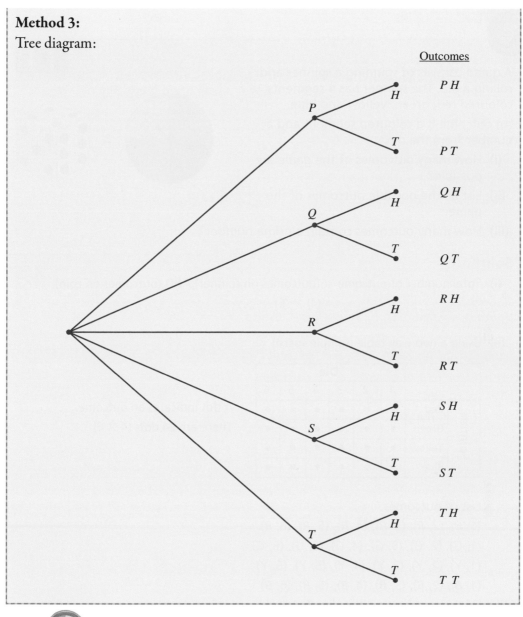

	Outcomes
H	P H
T	P T
H	Q H
T	Q T
H	R H
T	R T
H	S H
T	S T
H	T H
T	T T

exam
focus

Die:

A die is a cube with dots on each side.

The dots represent numbers from 1 to 6.

The numbers on the opposite sides of a die add up to 7.

A fair die is equally likely to land on any of the numbers from 1 to 6.

Dice is the plural of die.

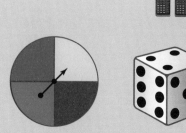

A game consists of spinning a spinner and rolling a die. The spinner has 4 segments coloured red, green, yellow and blue.

An outcome is a coloured segment and a number from the die.

(i) How many outcomes of the game are possible?

(ii) List all the possible outcomes of the game.

(iii) How many outcomes contain a prime number?

Solution

(i) Total number of outcome = (outcomes on spinner) AND (outcomes on coin)

$$= (4) \times (6)$$
$$= 24$$

(ii) Using a two-way table (sample space):

		Die					
		1	2	3	4	5	6
Spinner	Red	●	●	●	●	●	●
	Green	●	●	●	●	●	●
	Yellow	●	●	●	●	●	●
	Blue	●	●	●	●	●	●

A dot indicates an outcome.

There are 24 dots (4 × 6).

List of outcomes:

(1, R), (2, R), (3, R), (4, R), (5, R), (6, R)

(1, G), (2, G), (3, G), (4, G), (5, G), (6, G)

(1, Y), (2, Y), (3, Y), (4, Y), (5, Y), (6, Y)

(1, B), (2, B), (3, B), (4, B), (5, B), (6, B)

(iii) Of the numbers on the die, 2, 3 and 5 are prime numbers.

The 12 outcomes containing a prime number are:

(2, R), (2, G), (2, Y), (2, B)

(3, R), (3, G), (3, Y), (3, B)

(5, R), (5, G), (5, Y), (5, B)

Therefore, there are 12 outcomes which contain a prime number.

9 Probability

aims

- ☐ To understand that probabilities are measured on a scale from 0 to 1
- ☐ To be able to calculate the probability of an event occurring
- ☐ To understand the difference between theoretical and experimental probabilities
- ☐ To be able to use sample spaces, tree diagrams and Venn diagrams to calculate probabilities

Probability involves the study of the laws of chance. It is a measure of the chance, or likelihood, of something happening.

If you carry out an operation, or experiment, using coins, dice, spinners or cards, then each toss, throw, spin or draw is called a **trial**.

The possible things that can happen from a trial are called **outcomes**.

The outcomes of interest are called an **event**. In other words, an event is the set of successful outcomes.

key point

You need to understand all of these terms: **Probability, Trial, Outcome, Event.**

For example, if you throw a die and you are interested in the probability of throwing an even number, then the event is 2, 4, 6 – the successful outcomes.

If E is an event, then $P(E)$ stands for the probability that the event occurs. $P(E)$ is read as 'the probability of E'.

The probability of an event is a number between 0 and 1, including 0 and 1.

$$0 \leq P(E) \leq 1$$

The value of $P(E)$ can be given as a fraction, decimal or percentage.

Note: $P(E) = 0$ means that an event is **impossible**.
   $P(E) = 1$ means that an event is **certain**.

key point

Probability can **never** be a negative value.

The chance of an event happening can be shown on a **probability scale**:

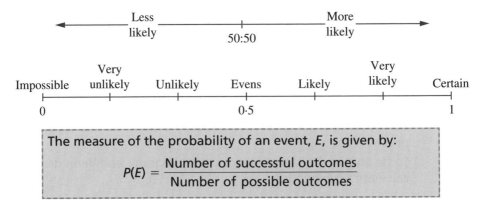

The measure of the probability of an event, E, is given by:

$$P(E) = \frac{\text{Number of successful outcomes}}{\text{Number of possible outcomes}}$$

Probability of an event not happening

If E is any event, then 'not E' is the event that E does not occur. Clearly, E and 'not E' cannot occur at the same time. Either E or 'not E' must occur. Thus, we have the following relationship between the probabilities of E and 'not E':

$P(E) + P(\text{not}\,E) = 1$
or
$P(\text{not }E) = 1 - P(E)$

Example

A bag contains three red, three green and four blue marbles. A marble is selected at random from the bag.

(i) What is the probability of selecting a blue marble?

(ii) What is the probability of selecting a green marble?

(iii) What is the probability of selecting a marble which is not green?

Solution

(i) $P(\text{Blue marble}) = \dfrac{\text{Number of blue marbles}}{\text{Total number of marbles}}$

$P(\text{Blue marble}) = \dfrac{4}{10} = \dfrac{2}{5}$

key point

'Drawn at random' means that every item is equally likely to be drawn.

(ii) $P(\text{Green marble}) = \dfrac{\text{Number of green marbles}}{\text{Total number of marbles}}$

$P(\text{Green marble}) = \dfrac{3}{10}$

(iii) $P(\text{not green marble}) = \dfrac{\text{Number of marbles which are not green}}{\text{Total number of marbles}}$

$P(\text{not green marble}) = \dfrac{7}{10}$

Alternative method:

$P(\text{not green marble}) = 1 - P(\text{green marble})$

$P(\text{not green marble}) = 1 - \dfrac{3}{10}$

$P(\text{not green marble}) = \dfrac{7}{10}$

Example

The net of a cube is shown. This net is cut from cardboard and folded to make a cube. Each face of the cube has the letter A, B or C on it. The cube is then rolled and the side facing upwards is called the outcome.

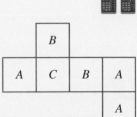

(i) What is the probability that the outcome will be A?

(ii) What is the probability that the outcome will be B?

(iii) What is the probability that the outcome will be C?

Solution

(i) $P(A) = \dfrac{\text{Number of faces with } A}{\text{Total number of faces}} = \dfrac{3}{6} = \dfrac{1}{2}$

(ii) $P(B) = \dfrac{\text{Number of faces with } B}{\text{Total number of faces}} = \dfrac{2}{6} = \dfrac{1}{3}$

(iii) $P(C) = \dfrac{\text{Number of faces with } C}{\text{Total number of faces}} = \dfrac{1}{6}$

Notice the link here between probability and the topic of area, nets and volume.

Three athletes, Alan, Barry and Colm are equally likely to win a 3-man race.

(i) List all the ways in which the men can finish, assuming all finish the race and there is no dead-heat.

(ii) What is the probability that they finish in the order: Barry, Alan, Colm?

(iii) What is the probability that Colm wins?

(iv) What is the probability that Alan finishes last?

Solution

(i) Let A = Alan, B = Barry and C = Colm. The athletes can finish in the following orders:

$$ABC, \quad ACB, \quad BAC, \quad BCA, \quad CAB, \quad CBA$$

(ii) $P(BAC) = \dfrac{\text{Number of arrangements with } BAC}{\text{Total number of arrangements}} = \dfrac{1}{6}$

(iii) $P(\text{Colm wins}) = \dfrac{\text{Number of arrangements with } C \text{ first}}{\text{Total number of arrangements}} = \dfrac{2}{6} = \dfrac{1}{3}$

(iv) $P(\text{Alan last}) = \dfrac{\text{Number of arrangements with } A \text{ at end}}{\text{Total number of arrangements}} = \dfrac{2}{6} = \dfrac{1}{3}$

A fair circular spinner consists of three sectors. Two are coloured blue and one is coloured red.

The spinner is spun and a fair coin is tossed.

(i) What is the probability of the spinner landing on a blue sector?

(ii) Find the probability of getting a head and a red.

(iii) Find the probability of getting a tail and a blue.

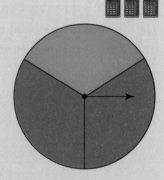

Solution

(i) $P(\text{blue sector}) = \dfrac{\text{Number of blue sectors}}{\text{Total number of sectors}}$

$P(\text{blue sector}) = \dfrac{2}{3}$

(ii) $P(\text{head and a red sector}) = P(\text{head}) \times P(\text{red})$

$P(\text{head and a red sector}) = \dfrac{1}{2} \times \dfrac{1}{3}$

$P(\text{head and a red sector}) = \dfrac{1}{6}$

(iii) $P(\text{tail and a blue sector}) = P(\text{tail}) \times P(\text{blue})$

$P(\text{tail and a blue sector}) = \dfrac{1}{2} \times \dfrac{2}{3}$

$P(\text{tail and a blue sector}) = \dfrac{1}{3}$

key point

Remember: 'and' means to multiply the outcomes.

Example

The probabilities of four events have been marked on a probability scale.

- Event *P*: A person is over 4 metres tall
- Event *Q*: A coin lands tails up
- Event *R*: Getting a score less than 7 on one roll of a die
- Event *S*: Pick a number greater than 1 from 1, 2, 3 and 4

Label the arrows with the letters *P*, *Q*, *R* and *S* to show the event they represent.

Solution

Determine the probability of each event.

Event *P*: A person is over 4 metres tall

The tallest man on Earth is approximately 2·7 metres tall, so it is not possible for a person to be 4 metres tall. Therefore, the probability of Event *P* occurring is 0.

> **key point**
>
> You must be able to calculate the probability of an event happening on the scale from 0 to 1.

Event *Q*: A coin lands tails up

A coin has two faces, head and tails, and it is equally likely to land on either of them. Therefore, the probability of Event *Q* occurring is 0·5.

Event *R*: Getting a score less than 7 on one roll of a die

All values on a die are less than 7, so it is a certainty that the die will land on a number less than 7. Therefore, the probability of Event *R* occurring is 1.

Event *S*: Pick a number greater than 1 from 1, 2, 3 and 4

There are three numbers greater than 1, so there is a 3 out of 4 chance of selecting a number greater than 1. Therefore, the probability of Event S occurring is $\frac{3}{4} = 0·75$.

Put these probabilities on the scale:

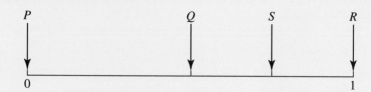

exam focus

You must know the structure of a deck of playing cards.

There are **52 cards** in a deck of cards.

4 suits: **Red:** **Hearts** and **Diamonds**

Black: **Clubs** and **Spades**

Each suit has 13 cards : Ace, 2, 3, 4, 5, 6, 7, 8, 9, 10

Jack, Queen and King.

Jack, Queen and King are known as 'picture cards'.

exam Q

A, B, C, D and *E* represent the probabilities of certain events occurring.

(i) Write the probability of each of the events listed into the table below.

Event		Probability
A club is selected in a random draw from a pack of playing cards	*A*	
A tossed fair coin shows a tail on landing	*B*	
The sun will rise in the east tomorrow	*C*	
May will follow directly after June	*D*	
A randomly selected person was born on a Thursday	*E*	

(ii) Place each of the letters *A, B, C, D* and *E* at its correct position on the probability scale below.

$$\begin{array}{cc} \vdash & \dashv \\ 0 & 1 \end{array}$$

Solution

(i) **A:** $P(\text{Club}) = \dfrac{\text{Number of clubs}}{\text{Total number of cards}} = \dfrac{13}{52} = \dfrac{1}{4}$

B: $P(\text{Tail}) = \dfrac{\text{Number of tails}}{\text{Total number sides}} = \dfrac{1}{2}$

C: *P*(sun rising in the east) is a certainty, as the sun always rises in the east. Therefore, *P*(sun rising in the east) = 1

D: *P*(May will follow directly after June) is an impossibility, as May comes before June. Therefore, *P*(May will follow directly after June) = 0

E: $P(\text{Thursday}) = \dfrac{\text{Number of Thursdays}}{\text{Total number days in a week}} = \dfrac{1}{7}$

Completed table:

Event		Probability
A club is selected in a random draw from a pack of playing cards	A	$\dfrac{1}{4}$
A tossed fair coin shows a tail on landing	B	$\dfrac{1}{2}$ OR evens OR 50/50
The sun will rise in the east tomorrow	C	1 OR certain
May will follow directly after June	D	0 OR impossible
A randomly selected person was born on a Thursday	E	$\dfrac{1}{7}$

exam focus

If possible, give answer for probabilities as a fraction or a decimal and not a word. Giving answers such as 'likely' may not get full marks.

(ii) Entering *A, B, C, D* and *E* on the scale gives:

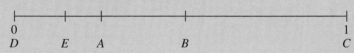

Example

(i) One hundred and fifty students sitting an examination were grouped according to age (16, 17 or 18) and gender (female or male). The results are given in the following table:

	Age 16	Age 17	Age 18
Female	30	18	12
Male	60	27	3

One student is chosen at random. What is the probability that the student is:
(a) Male? (b) A 16-year-old female? (c) Younger than 18? (d) Older than 19?

(ii) Label the probability of each event with the letters A, B, C and D, respectively. Indicate the position of A, B, C and D on the probability scale.

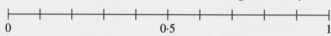

Solution

(i) (a) $P(\text{Male}) = \dfrac{\text{Number of males}}{\text{Total number of people}}$

$P(\text{Male}) = \dfrac{90}{150}$

$P(\text{Male}) = \dfrac{3}{5} = 0{\cdot}6$

(b) $P(16 \text{ yr old female}) = \dfrac{\text{Number of 16 yr old females}}{\text{Total number of people}}$

$P(16 \text{ yr old female}) = \dfrac{30}{150}$

$P(16 \text{ yr old female}) = \dfrac{1}{5} = 0{\cdot}2$

(c) $P(\text{Younger than 18}) = \dfrac{\text{Number of people younger than 18}}{\text{Total number of people}}$

$P(\text{Younger than 18}) = \dfrac{135}{150}$

$P(\text{Younger than 18}) = \dfrac{9}{10} = 0{\cdot}9$

(d) $P(\text{Older than 19}) = \dfrac{\text{Number of people older than 19}}{\text{Total number of people}}$

$P(\text{Older than 19}) = \dfrac{0}{150}$

$P(\text{Older than 19}) = 0$

(ii) Labelling the answers from (a), (b), (c) and (d) on the probability scale:

The percentage distribution of blood groups in the Irish population is given in the table below. The table also gives information about which types of blood can be safely used when people need to be given blood during an operation.

Blood Group	Percentage in Irish population	Blood groups to which transfusions can be safely given	Blood groups from which transfusions can be safely received
O−	8	All	O−
O+	47	O+, AB+, A+, B+	O+ and O−
A−	5	A−, A+, AB+, AB−	A− and O−
A+	26	A+ and AB+	A+, O−, O+, A−
B−	2	B−, B+, AB−, AB+	B− and O−
B+	9	B+ and AB+	B+, B−, O−, O+
AB−	1	AB− and AB+	AB−, O−, A−, B−
AB+	2	AB+	all

Source: Irish Blood Transfusion Service

(i) If an Irish person is chosen at random, what is the probability that the person will have blood group AB−?

(ii) Mary has blood group B−. If a person is chosen at random from the population, what is the probability that Mary could safely receive blood from that person?

(iii) Aaron has blood group O+ and donates blood. What is the probability that his blood can be given to a person randomly chosen from the population?

(iv) The Irish Blood Transfusion Service recently asked people with blood group O− to give blood as regularly as possible. Give a reason why this might be the case.

Solution

(i) $P(AB-) = 1\% = \dfrac{1}{100}$

(ii) From the table, because Mary has blood group B−, she can receive blood from blood groups B− or O−:

$$P(B- \text{ or } O-) = P(B-) + P(O-)$$
$$= 2\% + 8\%$$
$$= 10\% = \frac{10}{100} = \frac{1}{10}$$

Remember: 'or' means to add the outcomes.

(iii) Blood group O+ can be donated to O+, AB+, A+ and B+:

$$P(O+ \text{ or } AB+ \text{ or } A+ \text{ or } B+) = P(O+) + P(AB+) + P(A+) + P(B+)$$
$$= 47\% + 2\% + 26\% + 9\%$$
$$= 84\% = \frac{84}{100} = \frac{21}{25}$$

(iv) O− can receive blood only receive from other O− people. This is only 8% of the population, therefore this category needs to be encouraged to donate blood.

or

O− can safely give blood to all other groups and so is the best to have if there is any shortage of blood.

There are 80 members in a club. The table below shows the number of males and females who do or do not wear glasses:

	Male	Female	Total
Wearing glasses	4		12
Not wearing glasses		40	
Total	32		80

(i) Complete the table, by filling in the missing values.

(ii) A club member is selected at random. What is the probability that the club member is a:

(a) Male? (b) Person wearing glasses? (c) Female not wearing glasses?

(iii) A male from the club is selected at random.
What is the probability he wears glasses?

(iv) A member who wears glasses is selected at random.
What is the probability that it is a female?

(v) All members who wear glasses resign from the club. What is the probability that a club member now selected at random is male?

Solution

(i)

	Male	Female	Total
Wearing glasses	4	8	12
Not wearing glasses	28	40	68
Total	32	48	80

(ii) (a) $P(\text{Male}) = \dfrac{\text{Number of males}}{\text{Total number of people}} = \dfrac{32}{80} = \dfrac{2}{5}$

(b) $P(\text{Wearing glasses}) = \dfrac{\text{Number of people wearing glasses}}{\text{Total number of people}} = \dfrac{12}{80} = \dfrac{3}{20}$

(c) $P(\text{Female and no glasses}) = \dfrac{\text{Number of females with no glasses}}{\text{Total number of people}} = \dfrac{40}{80} = \dfrac{1}{2}$

(iii) A male is selected, so we will only consider the males when working out the probabilities:

$P(\text{Wearing glasses}) = \dfrac{\text{Number of males wearing glasses}}{\text{Total number of males}} = \dfrac{4}{32} = \dfrac{1}{8}$

(iv) A person wearing glasses is selected, so we will only consider the people with glasses when working out the probabilities:

$P(\text{Female}) = \dfrac{\text{Number of females wearing glasses}}{\text{Total number of people wearing glasses}} = \dfrac{8}{12} = \dfrac{2}{3}$

(v) All members with glasses leave, so now there are only 28 males and 40 females.

$P(\text{Male}) = \dfrac{\text{Number of males}}{\text{Total number of members}} = \dfrac{28}{28 + 40} = \dfrac{28}{68} = \dfrac{7}{17}$

Experimental probability

Often a probability can only be found by carrying out a series of experiments and recording the results. The probability of the event can then be **estimated** from these results. A probability found in this way is known as **experimental probability** or **relative frequency** of an event. Each separate experiment carried out is called a **trial**. To find the relative frequency, the experiment has to be repeated a number of times.

Estimating probabilities using relative frequency

> The relative frequency of an event in an experiment is given by:
>
> $P(E)$ = Relative frequency of an event = $\dfrac{\text{Number of successful trials}}{\text{Number of trials}}$

The expected number of outcomes (or expected value) is calculated as follows.

> Expected number of outcomes = (Relative frequency) × (Number of trials)
>
> or
>
> Expected number of outcomes = P(Event) × (Number of trials)

key point

If an experiment is repeated, there will be different outcomes. Increasing the number of times an experiment is repeated generally leads to better estimates of probability.

exam Q

In an experiment, Anne rolled a die 600 times.
The results are partially recorded in the table below.

Number on die	1	2	3	4	5	6
Frequency	92	101	115	98		105

(i) Calculate the number of times that a 5 appeared.

(ii) After looking at the results, Anne claims that the die is fair (unbiased). Do you agree with her? Give a reason for your answer.

(iii) If this die is rolled 300 times, how many times would you expect to get an even number as a result? Give a reason for your answer.

Solution

(i) $600 = 92 + 101 + 115 + 98 + x + 105$

   $600 = 511 + x$

 $600 - 511 = x$

    $89 = x$

Therefore, the number 5 was recorded 89 times.

(ii) Yes, I do agree that the die is fair. If the die is fair, out of 600 throws you would expect each number to show 100 times. Since the frequency of each number is close to 100, I do agree the die is fair.

OR

No, I do not agree that the die is fair. If the die is fair, out of 600 throws you would expect each number to show 100 times. Since the number 3 was recorded 115 times and the number 5 was recorded only 89 times, then I would conclude the die is not fair (biased).

(iii) Answer: 150

Reason: Half of the numbers on the die are even, therefore you would expect an even number to be thrown half of the number of times that the die was tossed.

OR

Answer: 152

Reason: Out of 600 rolls, an even value came up 304 times. Therefore, out of 300 rolls, we would expect 152 times.

The colour of 500 cars that pass a particular set of traffic lights during a two-hour period is recorded by a group of students.

Colour	Frequency	Relative frequency	Daily frequency (part (iii) below)
Red	70		
Blue	100		
Yellow	45		
White	55		
Black	90		
Silver	140		
Total	500		

(i) Calculate the relative frequency of each colour and write these into the table.

(ii) What is the probability that the next car to pass the lights is red?

(iii) Use the information to estimate the frequency of each colour if 2,400 cars pass the lights in a full day. Write this information into the table.

Solution

(i) Relative frequency $= \dfrac{\text{Number of successful trials}}{\text{Number of trials}}$

Colour	Frequency	Relative frequency	Daily frequency (part (iii) below)
Red	70	$\dfrac{70}{500} = \dfrac{7}{50}$	
Blue	100	$\dfrac{100}{500} = \dfrac{1}{5}$	
Yellow	45	$\dfrac{45}{500} = \dfrac{9}{100}$	
White	55	$\dfrac{55}{500} = \dfrac{11}{100}$	
Black	90	$\dfrac{90}{500} = \dfrac{9}{50}$	
Silver	140	$\dfrac{140}{500} = \dfrac{7}{25}$	
Total	500	1	

(ii) $P(\text{Red car}) = \dfrac{70}{500} = \dfrac{7}{50}$

(iii) Expected number of outcomes = (Relative frequency) × (Number of trials)

Colour	Frequency	Relative frequency	Daily frequency
Red	70	$\dfrac{7}{50}$	$\dfrac{7}{50} \times 2{,}400 = 336$
Blue	100	$\dfrac{1}{5}$	$\dfrac{1}{5} \times 2{,}400 = 480$
Yellow	45	$\dfrac{9}{100}$	$\dfrac{9}{100} \times 2{,}400 = 216$
White	55	$\dfrac{11}{100}$	$\dfrac{11}{100} \times 2{,}400 = 264$
Black	90	$\dfrac{9}{50}$	$\dfrac{9}{50} \times 2{,}400 = 432$
Silver	140	$\dfrac{7}{25}$	$\dfrac{7}{25} \times 2{,}400 = 672$
Total	500	1	2,400

key point

Relative frequency does not equal theoretical probability. Relative frequency is the fraction of times something actually happens. Hence, **relative frequency is an estimate of the theoretical probability.**

The value for relative frequency gets closer to the theoretical probability, as the number of trials (frequency) increases.

exam Q

(i) What is the probability of getting a 1 when a fair die is tossed?

(ii) A fair die is tossed 500 times. The results are recorded in the table below.

Number on die	1	2	3	4	5	6
Frequency	70	82	86	90	91	81
Relative frequency						

Calculate the relative frequency of each outcome and write it into the table above. Give your answer correct to 2 decimal places.

(ii) Give a possible reason for the difference in value between the relative frequency for 1 in the table and your answer to part (i).

Solution

(i) $P(1) = \dfrac{1}{6} = 0.17$

(ii)

Number on die	1	2	3	4	5	6
Frequency	70	82	86	90	91	81
Relative frequency	$\dfrac{70}{500}$ $= 0.14$	$\dfrac{82}{500}$ $= 0.16$	$\dfrac{86}{500}$ $= 0.17$	$\dfrac{90}{500}$ $= 0.18$	$\dfrac{91}{500}$ $= 0.18$	$\dfrac{81}{500}$ $= 0.16$

(iii) Since the relative frequency (experimental probability) is less than the theoretical probability, the die may be biased towards the other numbers on the die.

exam Q

(i) (a) Two fair coins are tossed. What is the probability of getting two heads?

(b) Two fair coins are tossed 1,000 times. How often would you expect to get two heads?

(ii) Sile hands Padraig a fair coin and tells him to toss it ten times. She says that if he gets ten heads then she will give him a prize. The first nine tosses are all heads. How likely is it that the last toss will also be a head? Tick the correct answer and give a reason.

Extremely unlikely ☐   Fairly unlikely ☐

50–50 chance ☐   Fairly likely ☐

Almost certain ☐

Solution

(i) (a) $P(\text{head and head}) = \frac{1}{2} \times \frac{1}{2} = \frac{1}{4}$

(b) From (a), we would expect to get two heads $\frac{1}{4}$ of the time.

No. of times to get two heads $= \frac{1}{4} \times 1{,}000 = 250$ times

(ii) 50–50 chance ☑

Reason: Every time you toss a coin, you have a 50–50 chance of getting a head. It doesn't matter how many times the coin has landed on a head prior to that toss.

OR

Fairly likely ☑   Almost certain ☑

Reason: The fact on that the coin has landed on heads nine times in a row would indicate that the coin is not, in fact, a fair coin and so it would be fairly likely to land on a head again.

exam focus

You should notice that there were three possible answers accepted in the exam for this question. As is often the case with questions involving opinion, sometimes more than one answer may be valid.

Sample space

A sample space is the set of all possible outcomes. A sample space can be very useful for seeing all possible outcomes and working out any appropriate probabilities. A sample space can be represented by a list, a two-way table or a tree diagram. Sample spaces were covered in Chapter 8 on Fundamental Principles of Counting.

Example

A game consists of rolling two fair dice, one red and one blue.

(i) Draw a sample space of all possible outcomes.

(ii) What is the probability that the number on the red die is even?

(iii) What is the probability that the outcomes are the same on each die?

(iv) What is the probability that the sum of the outcomes is greater than 8?

(v) What is the probability that the difference of the outcomes is equal to 2?

Solution

(i) Sample space showing all possible outcomes:

		Red die					
		1	**2**	**3**	**4**	**5**	**6**
Blue die	**1**	1, 1	1, 2	1, 3	1, 4	1, 5	1, 6
	2	2, 1	2, 2	2, 3	2, 4	2, 5	2, 6
	3	3, 1	3, 2	3, 3	3, 4	3, 5	3, 6
	4	4, 1	4, 2	4, 3	4, 4	4, 5	4, 6
	5	5, 1	5, 2	5, 3	5, 4	5, 5	5, 6
	6	6, 1	6, 2	6, 3	6, 4	6, 5	6, 6

(ii) Mark the outcomes on the sample space, where the number on the red die is even:

$$P(\text{Red even}) = \frac{18}{36} = \frac{1}{2}$$

		Red die					
		1	**2**	**3**	**4**	**5**	**6**
Blue die	**1**	1, 1	(1, 2)	1, 3	(1, 4)	1, 5	(1, 6)
	2	2, 1	(2, 2)	2, 3	(2, 4)	2, 5	(2, 6)
	3	3, 1	(3, 2)	3, 3	(3, 4)	3, 5	(3, 6)
	4	4, 1	(4, 2)	4, 3	(4, 4)	4, 5	(4, 6)
	5	5, 1	(5, 2)	5, 3	(5, 4)	5, 5	(5, 6)
	6	6, 1	(6, 2)	6, 3	(6, 4)	6, 5	(6, 6)

(iii) Mark the outcomes on the sample space, where the numbers on the dice are equal (marked with a red dot ●):

$$P(\text{Equal outcomes}) = \frac{6}{36} = \frac{1}{6}$$

(iv) Mark the outcomes on the sample space, where the sum of the numbers is greater than 8 (marked with a green cross ✗):

$$P(\text{Sum} > 8) = \frac{10}{36} = \frac{5}{18}$$

Blue die		Red die					
		1	**2**	**3**	**4**	**5**	**6**
1		●		◆			
2			●		◆		
3		◆		●		◆	✗
4			◆		●	✗	◆✗
5				◆	✗	●✗	✗
6				✗	◆✗	✗	●✗

(v) Mark the outcomes on the sample space, where the difference of the numbers is equal to 2 (marked with a blue diamond ◆):

$$P(\text{Difference} = 2) = \frac{8}{36} = \frac{2}{9}$$

exam focus

It is not necessary to draw a new sample space for each part of a question. It is good practice to draw one sample space and then use different colours, or different symbols (or both, as in this example) to mark the relevant outcomes.

exam Q

A game consists of two spinners. One with four segments, numbered 1 to 4, and the second with five segments, numbered 1 to 5. The spinners are spun.

(i) Draw a sample space of all possible outcomes.

(ii) If the spinners are fair, what is the probability of getting two 4s?

(iii) If the spinners are fair, what is the probability the values on the spinners sum to 6?

(iv) Jason thinks that one of the spinners is not fair.

Describe an experiment that he could do to find out whether the spinner is fair.

Solution

(i) Sample space showing all possible outcomes:

		Spinner 1			
		1	2	3	4
Spinner 2	1	1, 1			1, 4
	2		2, 2		
	3				3, 4
	4	4, 1		4, 3	
	5				5, 4

The numbers in the grid represent all the possible outcomes. A few have been filled in for you to understand what the grid represents.

To complete the solution you need to fill in all of the boxes.

(ii) There is only one outcome in which **both** spinners land on four:

$$P(\text{Both spinners land on 4}) = \frac{\text{Number of favourable outcomes}}{\text{Total number of outcomes}} = \frac{1}{20}$$

(iii) Use the same space to determine which outcomes will give a sum of 6. These are shaded in the grid.

$$P(\text{Sum of six}) = \frac{\text{Number where sum is 6}}{\text{Total number of outcomes}}$$

$$P(\text{Sum of six}) = \frac{4}{20}$$

$$P(\text{Sum of six}) = \frac{1}{5}$$

		Spinner 1			
		1	2	3	4
Spinner 2	1				
	2				2, 4
	3			3, 3	
	4		4, 2		
	5	5, 1			

(iv) Jason should spin the spinner he thinks is not fair many times (60 or more spins) and record the number it lands on. Consider the first spinner, if it is fair, it should land on each number, from 1 to 4, approximately the same number of times. That is, it should land on each number approximately one-quarter of the time.

Tree diagrams

We can also construct a probability tree diagram to help us solve some probability problems. A probability tree diagram shows all the possible events.

key point

To calculate the probability along a path, you multiply all probabilities along the branches on that path.

Example

A bowl of fruit contains 8 apples and 4 bananas.

(i) Jake choses a piece of fruit at random. Find the probability that he chooses an apple.

(ii) Jake chooses a piece of fruit and eats it. He then chooses a 2nd piece of fruit.

(a) Draw a tree diagram to show all possible outcomes for the pieces of fruit Jake can select.

(b) Use the tree diagram to find the probability that Jake chooses an apple followed by a banana.

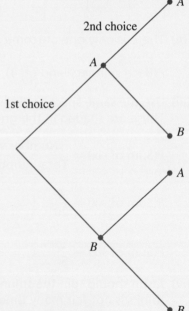

Solution

(i) $P(\text{Apple}) = \dfrac{\text{Number of apples}}{\text{Total number of fruit}}$

$= \dfrac{8}{12} = \dfrac{2}{3}$

(ii) (a) Tree diagram:

Where A = apple and B = banana

(b) Put the appropriate probabilities on each branch of the tree:

After the first choice, there will only be 11 pieces of fruit in the bowl.

If an apple is selected first, there are only 7 apples left to choose out of 11 pieces. So, the probability of selecting an apple after one apple has already been selected is $\frac{7}{11}$.

Apply this same logic to all branches, to work out each probability.

Using the tree diagram we see:

$$P(\text{apple then a banana}) = \frac{8}{12} \times \frac{4}{11}$$

$$= \frac{32}{132} = \frac{8}{33}$$

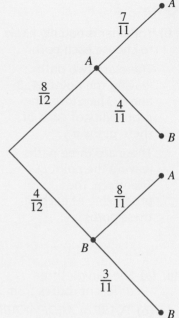

The arrows represent the different routes that a skier can take when skiing down a mountain. The circles on the diagram represent different points on the routes.

(i) When leaving any particular point on the mountain, a skier is **equally likely** to choose any of the available routes from the point.

Fill in the boxes in the diagram which represent the probability that the skier will take that route.

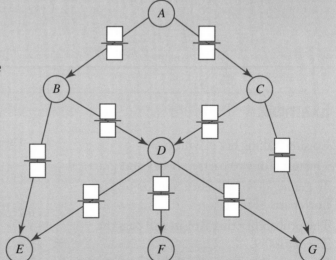

(ii) (a) If the skier starts at point *A*, in how many different ways can the skier reach point *E*?

(b) If the skier starts at point *A*, find the probability that the skier will reach point *E*.

Solution

(i) The skier is equally likely to choose each path.

There are two paths leaving the points A, B and C. Therefore, the probability of each of these paths is $\frac{1}{2}$.

There are three paths leaving the point D. Therefore, the probability of each of these paths is $\frac{1}{3}$.

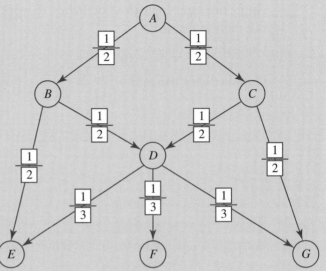

(ii) (a) She can go three different routes from A to E: ABE, ACDE, ABDE

(b) P(ABE or ACDE or ABDE) = P(ABE) + P(ABDE) + P(ACDE)

$$P(ABE) = \frac{1}{2} \times \frac{1}{2} = \frac{1}{4}$$

$$P(ABDE) = \frac{1}{2} \times \frac{1}{2} \times \frac{1}{3} = \frac{1}{12}$$

$$P(ACDE) = \frac{1}{2} \times \frac{1}{2} \times \frac{1}{3} = \frac{1}{12}$$

$$\therefore P(ABE \text{ or } ACDE \text{ or } ABDE) = \frac{1}{4} + \frac{1}{12} + \frac{1}{12}$$

$$\therefore P(ABE \text{ or } ACDE \text{ or } ABDE) = \frac{5}{12}$$

Example

Roisin is taking her driving test.

The test is in two parts: Theory and Practical.

To get her driving licence, she has to pass **both** parts of the test.

The probability that Roisin will pass the Theory is 0·9.

The probability that she will pass the Practical is 0·8.

If she fails her Theory she cannot take the Practical.

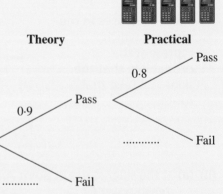

(i) Complete the tree diagram.

(ii) Calculate the probability that Roisin fails the driving test.

Solution

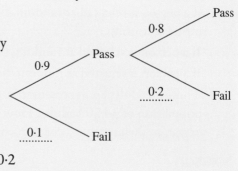

(i) **Theory exam:**

The probability Roisin passes the Theory exam is 0·9, so the probability she fails the Theory exam is $1 - 0·9 = 0·1$

Practical exam:

The probability Roisin passes the Practical exam is 0·8, so the probability she fails the Practical exam is $1 - 0·8 = 0·2$

(ii) There are two ways in which Roisin can fail the driving test:

(Fail the theory exam) or (Pass the theory exam and then fail the practical exam).

$P(\text{Fail}) = P(\text{Fail theory exam}) + P(\text{Pass theory exam and fail practical exam})$

$P(\text{Fail}) = 0·1 + (0·9 \times 0·2)$

$P(\text{Fail}) = 0·1 + 0·18$

$P(\text{Fail}) = 0·28$

Venn diagrams

Some situations can be presented clearly in a Venn diagram. This can then make it easier to work out the probabilities.

The topic of Sets is usually associated with Paper 1. However, you must be able to solve questions involving Sets when answering some probability questions.

Example

In a survey, 60 adults were asked whether or not they owned a car or a motorbike.

- 48 said they owned a car
- 22 said they owned a motorbike
- 9 people said they owned neither.

(i) Find how many adults owned both a car and a motorbike.

(ii) Represent the information in a Venn diagram.

(iii) If a person is selected at random, find the probability that they own a motorbike only.

(iv) If a person is selected at random, find the probability that they own a car.

(v) If a person is selected at random, find the probability that they do not own a car.

(vi) These 60 adults are representative of the people within a town, with a population of 34,200 adults. How many of the adults in this town would you expect to own neither a car nor a motorbike?

Solution

(i) If 9 people own neither a car nor a motorbike, then 51 $(60 - 9)$ must own either a car or a motorbike, or both.

48 people own a car and 22 people own a motorbike. $48 + 22 = 70$

$70 - 51 = 19$ people have been counted twice and therefore 19 people own **both** a car and a motorbike.

(ii) Entering the information into a Venn diagram:

$48 - 19 = 29$

$22 - 19 = 3$

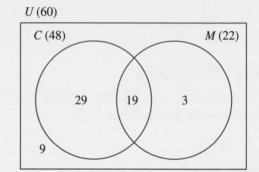

(iii) $P(\text{Motorbike only}) = \dfrac{\text{Number of people who own a motorbike only}}{\text{Total number of people}} = \dfrac{3}{60} = \dfrac{1}{20}$

(iv) $P(\text{Car}) = \dfrac{\text{Number of people who own a car}}{\text{Total number of people}} = \dfrac{48}{60} = \dfrac{4}{5}$

(v) $P(\text{Not a car}) = 1 - P(\text{Car})$

$P(\text{Not a car}) = 1 - \dfrac{4}{5} = \dfrac{1}{5}$

(vi) Expected number of outcomes $= (\text{Relative frequency}) \times (\text{Number of trials})$

$$= \dfrac{9}{60} \times (34{,}200)$$

$= 5{,}130$ adults would own neither a car nor a motorbike

35 people coming back from America were asked if they had
visited New York, Boston or San Francisco. The results were as follows:

- 20 had visited New York.
- 13 had visited Boston.
- 16 had visited San Francisco.
- 7 had been to all three cities.
- 3 had been to both New York and San Francisco, but not to Boston.
- 1 had been to both New York and Boston, but not to San Francisco.
- 8 had been to Boston and San Francisco.

(i) Display this information in a Venn diagram.

(ii) If one person is chosen at random from the group, what is the probability that the person had not visited any of the three cities?

(iii) If one person is chosen at random, what is the probability that the person had visited New York only?

(iv) If one person is chosen at random, what is the probability that the person had visited Boston or New York?

Solution

(i) Entering the information into a Venn diagram:

It is assumed here that you know how to complete a Venn diagram. For a comprehensive explanation on how to complete Venn diagrams, see the Sets chapter in *Less Stress More Success, Junior Cert, Higher Level, Paper 1.*

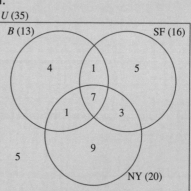

(ii) $P(\text{Not visited any city}) = \dfrac{\text{Number who visited none of the cities}}{\text{Total number of people}} = \dfrac{5}{35} = \dfrac{1}{7}$

(iii) $P(\text{New York only}) = \dfrac{\text{Number who visited New York only}}{\text{Total number of people}} = \dfrac{9}{35}$

(iv) $P(\text{Boston or New York}) = \dfrac{\text{Number who visited Boston or New York}}{\text{Total number of people}} = \dfrac{25}{35} = \dfrac{5}{7}$

exam
Q

In a survey, 54 people were asked which political party they
had voted for in the last three elections. The results are as follows:
- 30 had voted for the Conservatives.
- 22 had voted for the Liberals.
- 22 had voted for the Republicans.
- 12 had voted for the Conservatives and for the Liberals.
- 9 had voted for the Liberals and for the Republicans.
- 8 had voted for the Conservatives and for the Republicans.
- 5 had voted for all three parties.

(i) Represent the information in a Venn diagram.
(ii) If one person is chosen at random, what is the probability that the person
chosen did not vote in any of the three elections?
(iii) If one person is chosen at random, what is the probability that the person
chosen voted for at least two different parties?
(iv) If one person is chosen at random, what is the probability that the person
chosen voted for the same party in all three elections?

Solution

(i) Entering the information into a Venn
diagram:

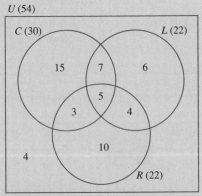

(ii) P(Did not vote in any election)$= \dfrac{\text{Number of people who did not vote}}{\text{Total number of people}}$

$$= \frac{4}{54} = \frac{2}{27}$$

(iii) P(At least two different parties)$= \dfrac{\text{Number of people who voted for 2 or 3 parties}}{\text{Total number of people}}$

$$= \frac{3 + 7 + 4 + 5}{54} = \frac{19}{54}$$

(iv) P(Same party in all three elections) $= P(C \text{ only}) + P(L \text{ only}) + P(R \text{ only})$

$$= \frac{15}{54} + \frac{6}{54} + \frac{10}{54}$$

$$= \frac{31}{54}$$

10 Statistics I: Statistical Investigations

aims
- ☐ To know the types of statistical data
- ☐ To be familiar with the terms used in studying statistics, referring to the glossary of statistical terms at the back of this book
- ☐ To learn what is required when gathering and interpreting statistical data

Introduction to statistics

Statistics deals with the collection, presentation, analysis and interpretation of data.

Social scientists, psychologists, pollsters, medical researchers, governments and many others use statistical methodology to study behaviours of populations. A large part of any statistical investigation is the production of **data**.

In statistics, any collection of variables is called data.

Types of data

Primary and secondary data

Primary data (first-hand data) are data that you collect yourself or are collected by someone under your direct supervision.

Secondary data (second-hand data) is data that have already been collected and made available from an external source such as newspapers, government departments, organisations or the internet.

Primary and secondary data have advantages and disadvantages.

Data	Advantages	Disadvantages	Sources
Primary	• Know how it was obtained • Accuracy is also known	• Time consuming • Can be expensive	• Surveys • Experiments
Secondary	Easy and cheap to obtain	• Could be out of date • May have mistakes and be biased • Unknown source of collection	• The Internet • Central Statistics Office

Steps in a statistical investigation

All statistical investigations begin with a question.

The steps of the Data Handling Cycle are:

1. Pose a question
2. Collect data
3. Present and analyse the information.
4. Interpret the results

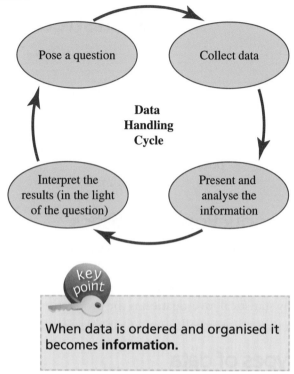

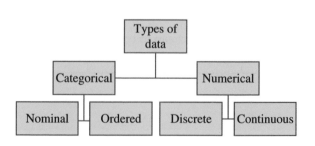

When data is ordered and organised it becomes **information.**

There are many ways to collect data, e.g. surveys, observations, experiments, Census at School, Wikipedia, etc.

It is vital when you are collecting data that your survey or source is **fair** and avoids **bias**.

Types of questions

When puting a question, you should avoid questions such as: Do you agree the economy is in a very poor state?

This is a leading question and may lead to a biased response.

You should also avoid using sources that are not reliable, such as an internet site that stated 75% of people believe the government of Fiji will destroy the moon on Friday. Conclusions based on such sources will be unreliable.

Types of data

Data can be divided into two broad categories:

- Categorical data
- Numerical data.

These two categories are also subdivided in two as indicated.

Categorical data

Unordered categorical data	Ordered categorical data
Unordered categorical data are data that can be counted but only described in words without any order or ranking.	Ordered categorical data are data that can be counted but only described in words and have an order or ranking.
Examples are colours, names, type of car and gender (male or female).	Examples are examination grades, football divisions and income groups.

Numerical data

Discrete numerical data	Continuous numerical data
Discrete numerical data are data which can only have certain values.	Continuous data are data which can take any numerical value within a certain range.
Examples are the number of students in a school, number of goals scored in a match and shoe sizes (including half-sizes).	Examples are time, weight, height, temperature, pressure and area. (Accuracy depends on the measuring device used.)

- Categorical data may also be referred to as qualitative data.
- Numerical data may also be referred to as quantitative data.

Example

Classify each of the following variables in terms of data type:

   (i) Colours of flowers

  (ii) Number of bicycles owned by students in your school

 (iii) Ages of students in a primary school

 (iv) Volumes of contents of water bottles

  (v) Countries of birth of Irish citizens

 (vi) Number of strokes to complete a round of golf

 (vii) Proportions of faulty fridges in samples of size fifty

(viii) Diameter of tennis balls

 (ix) Examination grades

  (x) Makes of TV in a salesroom.

Solution

   (i) Categorical, unordered

  (ii) Numerical, discrete

 (iii) Numerical, continuous (but age in years is discrete)

 (iv) Numerical, continuous

  (v) Categorical, unordered

 (vi) Numerical, discrete

 (vii) Numerical, discrete

(viii) Numerical, continuous

 (ix) Categorical, ordered

  (x) Categorical, unordered

Populations and samples

To find out the average weight of men in Ireland, we could, in theory, measure them all. In practice, this would be almost impossible to do. It would take too long and cost too much. Instead, we can measure the weights of a sample. Provided the sample is carefully chosen, we can obtain almost as much information from the sample as from measuring the weight of every man in Ireland.

In statistics, we distinguish between a **population** and a **sample**.

key point

A population is all the possible data and a sample is part of the data.

The population is all the possible data

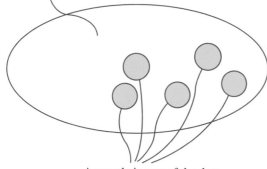

A sample is part of the data

key point

A sample is a small part of the population selected for surveying. A random sample is a sample in which every member of the population has an equal chance of being selected, and the selections are made independently.

Sampling is useful because it reduces the amount of data you need to collect and process. It also allows you to carry out a test without involving all the population.

An Irish sports journalist intends to write a book about the English Football Premiership. She will analyse all Premiership matches in the season. For each match, she records whether it is a home win, an away win or a draw. She also records, for each match, the total number of goals scored and the amount of time played before a goal is scored. Reference books showed that in the previous season, the mean number of goals per game was 2·345. On the first weekend of the season, she recorded the number of goals scored in each match and calculated the mean number of goals per match as 2·6.

After carefully reading the above passage, identify an example of:

(i) A population		**(v)** A continuous variable	
(ii) A sample		**(vi)** Primary data	
(iii) A qualitative variable		**(vii)** Secondary data.	
(iv) A discrete variable			

Solution

(i) Populations mentioned in the passage will relate to all Premiership matches played in the season and include either the results, the total number of goals or the amounts of time played before a goal is scored.

(ii) A sample would be the total number of goals scored in each match played, for example, in the fourth weekend of the season.

(iii) A qualitative variable would be the result of matches Home Win (H), Away Win (A), Draw (D).

(iv) A discrete variable would be the number of goals scored in each match.

(v) A continuous variable would be the amount of time played before a goal is scored.

(vi) Primary data would be the data the journalist collected in that season.

(vii) Secondary data (obtained from a reference book) would be the mean number of goals per game in the previous season.

Sampling without bias

When you are selecting a sample, you need to avoid **bias** – anything which makes the sample unrepresentative. For example, if you want to estimate how often residents of Waterford visit the cinema in a year, it would be foolish to stand outside a cinema as the audience is coming out and ask people as they pass. This would give a biased sample, as all the people you ask would have been to the cinema at least once that year. You can avoid bias by taking a random sample.

Reliability of data

When choosing a sample it is vital you ensure that:

- The random sample is picked from the whole population
- Every member of the population has an equal chance of being selected
- The sample is large enough.

One method of selecting a random sample is to assign a number to every member of the population and then use your calculator to generate a set of random numbers. A member becomes part of the sample if their number corresponds to one of the numbers in the generated set.

A spreadsheet application or 'picking names from a hat' will also achieve a random sample.

Tallying and frequency tables

One way data can be sorted easily is by using **a frequency table**.

A frequency table shows how frequently each piece of data occurs. It is good practice to include a tally row in your frequency table. Tallies are marks to help you keep track of counts. The marks are bunched together in groups of five.

When using tallies:

$$||| = 3 \qquad \cancel{||||} = 5 \qquad \cancel{||||} \, || = 7 \qquad \cancel{||||} \; \cancel{||||} \, || = 12$$

Jack goes to an all-boys school. He decides to carry out a survey to determine the amount of time students spend on the internet per week. Jack chose 30 students at random from his own school register and asked each of these students the time, to the nearest hour, they spend on the internet. The raw data were recorded as follows.

8	15	0	9	22	11	8	17	17	23
1	7	10	15	16	20	22	19	4	2
12	15	18	18	18	4	9	20	21	0

Complete the following grouped frequency table.

Time spent on the internet	0–4	5–9	10–14	15–19	20–24
Tally					
Number of students					

(i) Is this primary or secondary data? Give a reason for your answer.

(ii) Is the data discrete or continuous? Explain your answer.

(iii) Jack's friend Jim says, 'A large sample will always give a better estimate of what we are trying to measure for the population, regardless of how it is chosen.' Do you agree with Jim? Justify your opinion.

(iv) Can you identify two possible sources of bias in Jack's survey?

(v) Suggest two ways Jack could improve his sample to make it more representative nationally.

Solution

Time spent on the internet	0–4	5–9	10–14	15–19	20–24
Tally	ЖHІ І	ЖHІ	ІІІ	ЖHІ ЖHІ	ЖHІ І
Number of students	6	5	3	10	6

(i) This is primary data, as Jack collected the data himself.

(ii) Times are rounded to the nearest hour. This is discrete data.

(iii) I disagree with Jim because a larger sample which is not representative of the underlying population will not give a better estimate of what we are trying to measure for the population. It must first be a random sample, where every item in the population has an equal probability of being selected in the sample.

(iv) Some examples of sources of bias:
- Only boys in the survey ⇒ gender bias
- Only one school surveyed ⇒ may not be representative of the population as a whole
- Survey may not have been answered honestly, e.g. students may understate internet time if they are embarrassed to admit the actual time spent on the internet.

(v) Some examples of how to improve his sample:
- Include an all-girls school
- Include a coeducation school
- Include schools from outside the area
- Improve questions to eliminate over/underestimates from students
- Take account of how different age groups affect the result.

11 Statistics II: Central Tendency and Spread of Data

aims

☐ To know mean, mode and median are all measures of average/central tendency

☐ To learn how to calculate them, both from lists of numbers or from frequency distribution tables

☐ To know about lower quartile and upper quartile

☐ To know about measures of spread and how to calculate range and interquartile range. These calculations can apply to lists of numbers or frequency distribution tables.

☐ To be able to apply mid-interval values to calculate the mean

☐ To learn how to handle questions linking statistics to other sections of our maths course or to in-context questions

Averages

There are many types of averages. Three that we meet initially are called the **mean**, the **mode** and the **median**. They are also known as measures of central tendency.

Mean

The mean is the correct name for what most people call the average.

key point

> The mean of a set of values is defined as the sum of all the values divided by the number of values.

That is:

$$\text{Mean} = \frac{\text{Sum of all the values}}{\text{Number of values}}$$

The formula is often written as: $\mu = \dfrac{\Sigma x}{n}$ (*see* booklet of formulae and tables page 33)

Note: Σ, pronounced sigma, means the sum of (i.e. Σx means 'add up all the x-values').

μ, pronounced mew, is the symbol for the mean.

Mode

The mode of a set of items is the item that occurs most often. If there are no repeated items, then the mode does not exist.

Median

When the values are arranged in ascending or descending order of size, then the median is the middle value. If the number of values is even, then the median is the mean of the two middle values.

Note: Half the values lie below the median and half the values lie above the median. The median is also called the second quartile (Q_2).

Example

The ages of the seven dwarfs are as follows.

Name	Happy	Doc	Sleepy	Sneezy	Dopey	Grumpy	Bashful
Age	685	702	498	539	402	685	619

(i) Find the mean age.

(ii) Find the (mode) modal age.

(iii) Find the median age.

Solution

(i) Mean age $= \dfrac{\text{Sum of all their ages}}{\text{Number of dwarfs}} = \dfrac{\Sigma x}{n}$

$$\text{Mean} = \frac{685 + 702 + 498 + 539 + 402 + 685 + 619}{7}$$

$$\mu = \text{Mean} = \frac{4{,}130}{7} = 590$$

(ii) Mode $= 685$ The number that occurs most often

                         (Happy and Grumpy are twins!)

(iii) Median $=$ middle value in ascending or descending order

         $= 702, 685, 685, \mathbf{619}, 539, 498, 402$

         $= 619$

The mean and the median need not necessarily be members of the original set of values, while the mode, if it exists, is always a member of the original set of values.

A note on averages

Average	Advantages	Disadvantages
Mean	• Useful for further analysis • Uses all the data • Easy to calculate	• Distorted by extreme results • Mean is not always a given data value
Mode	• Easy to find • Not influenced by extreme values • Is the only measure suitable for qualitative nominal data	• Not very useful for further analysis • May not exist
Median	• Useful for further analysis • Unaffected by extremes • Easy to calculate if data are ordered	• Not always a given data value • Can be difficult to calculate

Example

Write down a set of five positive integers with:
  (i) Mean of 8
 (ii) Mean of 8 and mode of 3
(iii) Mean of 8, mode of 3 and median of 9
(iv) Mean of 8, mode of 3, median of 9 and range of 10

(Range = Highest value − Lower value)

Solution

To have a mean of 8 the five numbers must sum to 40.
  (i) $\{5, 6, 7, 8, 14\}$ or $\{1, 2, 3, 4, 30\}$ or lots of other choices
 (ii) $\{3, 3, 3, 14, 17\}$ or $\{3, 3, 7, 10, 17\}$ or $\{1, 2, 3, 3, 31\}$ or lots of other choices
(iii) $\{3, 3, 9, 10, 15\}$ fewer choices here
(iv) $\{3, 3, 9, 12, 13\}$ only one choice here

Example

A survey of a housing estate with 36 houses is undertaken by a city council.
The survey recorded the number of occupants per house as follows:

0	7	5	5	6	6	2	4	5	6	7	4
4	6	5	6	5	5	4	3	2	7	6	5
0	6	5	6	6	6	4	6	6	5	4	2

  (i) Represent the information in a frequency distribution table.
 (ii) Calculate the mean number of occupants per house.
(iii) What is the mode?
(iv) Suggest a reason why two houses recorded no occupants.
 (v) What insights can you draw from yours answers to (i) to (iv) as to the number
       of people, age distribution and social conditions in the estate?

Solution

  (i) Frequency distribution table

Number of occupants per house	0	1	2	3	4	5	6	7
Number of houses	2	0	3	1	6	9	12	3

 (ii) For a frequency distribution:

$$\text{Mean} = \mu = \frac{\Sigma fx}{\Sigma f} \qquad \text{(from booklet of formulae and tables page 33)}$$

$$= \frac{(2)(0) + (0)(1) + (3)(2) + (1)(3) + (6)(4) + (9)(5) + (12)(6) + (3)(7)}{2 + 0 + 3 + 1 + 6 + 9 + 12 + 3}$$

$$= \frac{0 + 0 + 6 + 3 + 24 + 45 + 72 + 21}{36} = \frac{171}{36} = 4{\cdot}75$$

Or you can use your calculator.

(iii) Mode = most common number = 6, which is recorded 12 times.

(iv) Two houses recorded no occupants because:

   • The houses were unoccupied for some reason (fire, vandalism, holidays)

   • There was no answer when the surveyors called

   • The houses were for sale

 (v) 171 people with a mean house occupancy of almost five (4·75) could indicate
     large young families (or extended families). Two unoccupied houses might
     indicate a somewhat derelict neighbourhood.

27 students in a class each recorded the amount of money they spent in the school shop during the Monday morning break. The total amount spent was €57·24.

(i) Find the mean amount spent per student during the Monday morning break.

(ii) One extra student joined the class and reported she spent €5·20 during the Monday morning break. Calculate the new mean including the extra student.

Solution

(i) Mean $= \dfrac{\text{Total amount spent}}{\text{Total number of students}} = \dfrac{57\cdot24}{27} = $ €2·12

(ii) Total for 28 students $=$ €57·24 $+$ €5·20 $=$ €62·44

$$\text{New mean} = \frac{62\cdot44}{28} = \text{€2·23}$$

Given the mean

Often we are given the mean and we need to find one of the values or frequencies. In these cases, we are given an equation in disguise. We use this equation to find the missing value or frequency.

Example

The following frequency table shows the marks awarded to a class of students in a test.

Marks	1	2	3	4	5	6	7
Number of students	5	8	x	$x+2$	7	4	2

If the mean mark for the class was 3·6, find the value of x.

Solution

Equation in disguise: $\qquad\qquad\qquad\qquad\qquad$ Mean $= 3\cdot6 = \dfrac{36}{10}$

$$\therefore \frac{5(1) + 8(2) + x(3) + (x + 2)(4) + 7(5) + 4(6) + 2(7)}{5 + 8 + x + x + 2 + 7 + 4 + 2} = \frac{36}{10}$$

$$\frac{5 + 16 + 3x + 4x + 8 + 35 + 24 + 14}{2x + 28} = \frac{36}{10}$$

$$\frac{7x + 102}{2x + 28} = \frac{36}{10}$$

$$10(7x + 102) = 36(2x + 28)$$

$$70x + 1{,}020 = 72x + 1{,}008$$

$$12 = 2x$$

$$6 = x$$

The table below shows the distances travelled by seven paper airplanes after they were thrown.

Airplane	A	B	C	D	E	F	G
Distance (cm)	188	200	250	30	380	330	302

(a) Find the median of the data.

(b) Find the mean of the data.

(c) Airplane D is thrown again and the distance it travels is measured and recorded in place of the original measurement. The median of the data remains unchanged and the mean is now equal to the median. How far did airplane D travel the second time?

(d) What is the minimum distance that airplane D would need to have travelled in order for the median to have changed?

Solution

(a) Median = middle value of 30, 188, 200, **250**, 302, 330, 380.

Median = 250 cm

(b) Mean = $\dfrac{\text{Total distance travelled}}{\text{Number of aeroplanes}}$

$= \dfrac{30 + 188 + 200 + 250 + 302 + 330 + 380}{7}$

$= \dfrac{1,680}{7} = 240$ cm

(c) This is an equation in disguise.

Let x = Distance travelled by airplane D

Mean = $\dfrac{x + 188 + 200 + 250 + 302 + 330 + 380}{7}$

$\therefore 250 = \dfrac{x + 1650}{7}$ Mean = Median = 250 from part (a)

$1,750 = x + 1,650$

$100 = x$

(d) Airplane D, 188, 200, 250, 302, 330, 380

If airplane D is to be the median then 188, 200, 250, airplane D, 302, 330, 380.

By observation then the distance travelled by airplane D must be greater than 250 cm. That is because in order for the median to have changed airplane D must be the median or above the median.

- This question was worth a total of 25 marks.
- Part (a) was awarded 5 marks for the correct answer, which was 250 cm.
- Part (b) was awarded 10 marks and was very well answered by candidates.
- Parts (c) and (d) were very poorly answered and were together awarded the remaining 10 marks. However, 8 marks were awarded for: Greater than 250 cm. This reduced the marks available for the more challenging (c) part to 2 marks.
- Remember to watch your time budget and keep moving through the questions.

Two measures of spread

1. **The range:** The range is the difference between the highest data value and the lowest data value.

2. **The interquartile range:** Quartiles, as their name suggests, are the quarter-way divisions of the data.

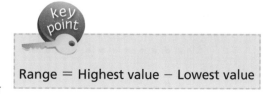

Range = Highest value − Lowest value

The **lower quartile**, Q_1, is the value one-quarter of the way through the distribution.
The **upper quartile**, Q_3, is the value three-quarters of the way through the distribution.

Here is a diagram to help clarify the situation.

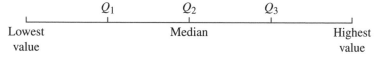

The **interquartile range** = upper quartile value − lower quartile value = $Q_3 - Q_1$.
Therefore, half the values in a distribution must lie between the upper and lower quartiles. The interquartile range is a number.

The interquartile range gives a measure of the spread of the values about the median.

The median is often referred to as Q_2.

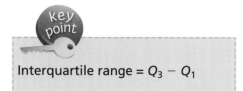

Interquartile range = $Q_3 - Q_1$

A box contains 50 cards. Each card has a number from 1 to 6 written on it. The following table shows the frequencies for each number.

(i) Calculate the value of k.

(ii) Find **(a)** The median

       (b) The interquartile range.

Number	1	2	3	4	5	6
Frequency	13	5	10	k	13	7

Solution

(i) $13 + 5 + 10 + k + 13 + 7 = 50$

$$48 + k = 50$$
$$k = 2$$

(ii) Put the data in a line plot as shown. One dot per card goes over each value. (More on line plots in Chapter 12, statistics III.)

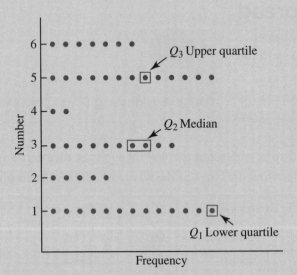

(a) Median (Q_2) is associated with the middle value $= \dfrac{3 + 3}{2} = 3$.

(b) Interquartile range = upper quartile − lower quartile

$$= Q_3 - Q_1$$
$$= 5 - 1$$
$$= 4$$

key point

For an even number of values, the median is the mean of the two middle values.

In summary, it is important to know that we have two ways of the measuring the variability or spread of a distribution:

- The range
- The interquartile range

Example

Find the mean and the range of the following sets of numbers:

(i) $4, 4, 4, 4, 4$

(ii) $1, 3, 3\frac{1}{2}, 4\cdot2, 8\cdot3$

(iii) $-196, -49, 25, 66, 174$

(iv) Hence, interpret what your answers imply.

Solution

(i) $\mu = \dfrac{4 + 4 + 4 + 4 + 4}{5} = \dfrac{20}{5} = 4$

    Range $= 4 - 4 = 0$

(ii) $\mu = \dfrac{1 + 3 + 3\frac{1}{2} + 4\cdot2 + 8\cdot3}{5} = \dfrac{20}{5} = 4$

    Range $= 8\cdot3 - 1 = 7\cdot3$

(iii) $\mu = \dfrac{-196 - 49 + 25 + 66 + 174}{5} = \dfrac{20}{5} = 4$

    Range $= 174 - (-196) = 174 + 196 = 370$

(iv) Interpretation:

    Each set has a mean $= 4$, and while set (i) has data that is not spread out at all, set (iii) has a higher range than set (ii), confirming that set (iii) has a wider spread than set (ii).

A test consisted of seven questions. One mark was awarded per question for a correct solution and no marks for an incorrect solution. The following distribution table shows how a class of students scored in the test.

Mark	0	1	2	3	4	5	6	7
Number of students	1	7	6	5	2	6	3	0

(i) Show that the mean mark scored was 3.

(ii) Five new students joined the class. The new students took the same test and achieved marks of 0, 1, 1, 3 and 7.

In each of the following questions, insert the correct letter in the box provided.

When the results of the five students were included with the original results:

(a) The mean mark for the class was:

X – unchanged Y – decreased Z – increased   Answer ☐

(b) The range for the class was:

X – unchanged Y – decreased Z – increased   Answer ☐

Justify your answer in each case.

Solution

(i) $$\frac{(1)(0) + (7)(1) + (6)(2) + (5)(3) + (2)(4) + (6)(5) + (3)(6) + (0)(7)}{1 + 7 + 6 + 5 + 2 + 6 + 3 + 0}$$

$$= \frac{0 + 7 + 12 + 15 + 8 + 30 + 18 + 0}{30}$$

$$= \frac{90}{30} = 3$$

(ii) (a) Answer $\boxed{Y}$ because the mean mark of the five new

students is $= \dfrac{0 + 1 + 1 + 3 + 7}{5} = \dfrac{12}{5} = 2 \cdot 4.$

Since $2 \cdot 4 < 3$, the original mean, we conclude that the addition of five new students decreased the mean.

(b) Answer $\boxed{Z}$ because one of the new students achieved a score of seven.

This new student increased the range from $6 - 0 = 6$ to $7 - 0 = 7$, thus the results were more spread out, which means the range was increased.

Grouped frequency distribution

We can estimate the mean of a grouped frequency distribution by taking the **mid-interval values** of each class. Otherwise, the procedure is the same as before.

Example

The frequency distribution below shows the number of hours per week spent watching television by 37 people.

Hours	0−2	2−6	6−12	12−20	20−30
No. of people	5	9	12	6	5

(**Note:** 0−2 means 0 is included but 2 is not and so on.)
Estimate the mean by taking the mid-interval values of each class.

Solution

We assume the data to be at mid-interval values.
It is good practice to rewrite the table using these mid-interval values.
New table:

Hours (mid-interval values)	1	4	9	16	25
No. of people	5	9	12	6	5

$$\text{Mean} = \mu = \frac{\Sigma fx}{\Sigma f} = \frac{5(1) + 9(4) + 12(9) + 6(16) + 5(25)}{5 + 9 + 12 + 6 + 5}$$

$$= \frac{370}{37} = 10$$

∴ The mean number of hours spent watching television per week is 10 hours.

The salaries, in €, of the different employees working in a call centre are listed below.

22,000	16,500	38,000	26,500	15,000	21,000	15,500	46,000
42,000	9,500	32,000	27,000	33,000	36,000	24,000	37,000
65,000	37,000	24,500	23,500	28,000	52,000	33,000	25,000
23,000	16,500	35,000	25,000	33,000	20,000	19,500	16,000

(a)   Use this data to complete the grouped frequency table below.

Salary (€1,000)	0–10	10–20	20–30	30–40	40–50	50–60	60–70
No. of Employees							

(Note: 10–20 means €10,000 or more but less than €20,000, etc.)

(b)   Using mid-interval values find the mean salary of the employees.

(c)   (i) Outline another method which could have been used to calculate the mean salary.

(ii) Which method is more accurate? Explain your answer.

Solution

(a)   From the given data we complete the table as follows:

Salary (€1,000)	0–10	10–20	20–30	30–40	40–50	50–60	60–70
No. of Employees	1	6	12	9	2	1	1

(b)

Mid-interval values	5	15	25	35	45	55	65
No. of Employees	1	6	12	9	2	1	1

$$\text{Mean} = \frac{(1)(5) + (6)(15) + (12)(25) + (9)(35) + (2)(45) + (1)(55) + (1)(65)}{1 + 6 + 12 + 9 + 2 + 1 + 1}$$

$$\text{Mean} = \frac{5 + 90 + 300 + 315 + 90 + 55 + 65}{32}$$

$$\text{Mean} = \frac{920}{32} = 28{\cdot}75$$

Mean =   €28,750 as figures given were salaries in thousands.

exam focus

Be sure to read the question carefully, understand what is asked and answer that question.

(c) (i) Another method is to add up all the actual salaries and divide that total by 32 (the number of employees).

exam focus

It is vital not to waste time here. You are asked to **outline** another method. So it is not necessary to do the calculations. Adding up 32 salaries would be very time consuming and would probably contain calculation errors.

(ii) The method that is most accurate is described above in (c) part (i).
The reason is that while the mid-interval value gives a very good approximation, the other method gives the exact answer.

key point

The exact answer $= \dfrac{\text{Total salaries}}{32} = \dfrac{917,000}{32} = €28,656·25$

is not required in this question.

exam Q

The size, mean and range of four sets of data, A, B, C and D, are given in this table:

	A	**B**	**C**	**D**
Size (n)	12	50	50	500
Mean (μ)	15	15	55	5
Range	40	50	22	15

Complete the sentences below by inserting the relevant letter in each space.
   (i) On average, the data in set _____ are the biggest numbers and the data in set _____ are the smallest numbers.
   (ii) The set that contains more numbers than any other is _____ and the set that contains fewer numbers than any other is _____.
   (iii) The set with the greatest total is _____.
   (iv) The data in set _____ have the greatest difference between their highest and lowest values.

Solution

(i) On average, the data in set _____C_____ are the biggest numbers and the data in set _____D_____ are the smallest numbers.

Set C has a mean = 55 which is by far the biggest.

(ii) The set that contains more numbers than any other is _____D_____ and the set that contains fewer numbers than any other is _____A_____.

D has 500 numbers, A has only 12 numbers.

(iii) A total $= 12 \times 15 = 180$
B total $= 50 \times 15 = 750$
C total $= 50 \times 55 = 2{,}750$
D total $= 500 \times 5 = 2{,}500$
∴ The set with the greatest total is _____C_____.

(iv) The data in set _____B_____(with a range of 50) have the greatest difference between their highest and lowest values.

12 Statistics III:
Representing Data

 aims
☐ To know how to construct and answer questions on bar charts, histograms, pie charts, stem and leaf diagrams, skewed and symmetric curves
☐ To cope with exam questions incorporating statistical information and displays

Diagrams

Many people find numerical data easier to understand if it is presented in a diagram. On this course, there are five ways of representing data in a diagram.

1. Bar charts
2. Line plots
3. Histogram
4. Stem and leaf plots
5. Pie charts

 key point

When drawing a statistical diagram, the following is important:
• Label both axes (where necessary) and include a title.
• Use scales that are easy to read and give a clear overall impression.

Bar charts

Bar charts are a simple and effective way of displaying categorical, ordinal and discrete data. The bars can be drawn vertically or horizontally. The height, or length, of each bar represents the frequency. Each bar must be the same width and leave the same space between the bars. The bar with the greatest height, or longest length, represents the mode.

 key point

A bar chart **cannot** be used to represent continuous data. This is the reason a gap is left between the bars.

Example

The spreadsheet below shows the number of different drinks purchased from a vending machine on a particular day.

	A	B
1	Drink	Number of drinks
2	Tea	17
3	Coffee	18
4	Chocolate	15
5	Soup	12
6	Other	13

(i) Represent the data with a bar chart.

(ii) What was the total number of drinks sold on the day?

(iii) Express the least popular drink as a percentage of the total number of drinks sold on the day.

Solution

(i) Bar chart: Number of different drinks purchased on a particular day.

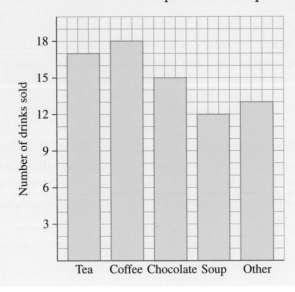

(ii) Total number of drinks sold $= 17 + 18 + 15 + 12 + 13 = 75$

(iii) Least popular drink was soup.

$$\text{Percentage of soup drinks sold} = \frac{\text{Number of soup drinks sold}}{\text{Total number of drinks sold}} \times 100\%$$

$$= \frac{12}{75} \times 100\% = 16\%$$

Line plots

For categorical, ordinal and discrete data (see glossary of statistical terms), use a line plot. This is similar to a bar chart, with the bars replaced with dots or Xs. A line plot is often called a **dot plot**. It is used for small sets of data, usually fewer than 50 values. It consists of a horizontal axis on which the values (or categories) are evenly marked, from the smallest value to the largest value, including any value in between that does not occur. Each value is indicated with a dot over the corresponding value on the horizontal axis. Each dot represents **one** value. The number of dots above each value indicates how many times each value occurs. Dots must be equally spaced over each value. Each dot is similar to a tally mark used in a frequency distribution. The main advantage of a line plot is that it can be created very quickly, even while collecting the data.

Example

In a survey, 32 people were asked how much money they spent each week on the National Lottery. The results, in €, are shown below:

| 0 | 2 | 2 | 4 | 0 | 4 | 6 | | 6 | 4 | 8 | | 10 | 6 | | 4 | 0 | 2 | 4 |
| 4 | 2 | 6 | 8 | 2 | 4 | 4 | | 10 | 6 | 4 | | 2 | 0 | | 4 | 6 | 8 | 2 |

(i) Complete the following data capture sheet:

Amount, in €	0	2	4	6	8	10
Tally						
Number of people						

(ii) Represent the data with a line plot.

(iii) Describe the shape of the line plot.

(iv) Write down the modal amount of money spent per week on the lottery for these 32 people.

Solution

(i) Complete the following data capture sheet:

Amount, in €	0	2	4	6	8	10
Tally	||||	ⅢⅡ ||	ⅢⅢⅢⅢ	ⅢⅢ |	|||	||
Number of people	4	7	10	6	3	2

(ii)

Amount spent on the national lottery

```
                      X
                      X
                      X
                X     X
                X     X     X
                X     X     X
        X       X     X     X
        X       X     X     X     X
        X       X     X     X     X     X
        X       X     X     X     X     X
     ┼─────┼─────┼─────┼─────┼─────┼
     0     2     4     6     8     10
              Amount, in €
```

key point

Dots (•) are often used instead of x (see the exam question on line plots in Chapter 11, Statistics II).

(iii) This line plot has a symmetric (balanced) shape,

(iv) The modal (most common) amount spent per week is €4.

Histogram

A histogram is often used to display information contained in a frequency distribution. The essential characteristic of a histogram is that the area of each rectangle represents the frequency, and the sum of the areas of the rectangles is equal to the sum of the frequencies.

Example

The histogram below shows the time spent by a group of women in a boutique.

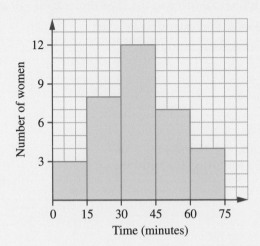

(i) Complete the following table.

Time (minutes)	0–15	15–30	30–45	45–60	60–75
Number of women					

(**Note:** 0–15 means 0 or more but less than 15, etc.)

(ii) How many women are in the group?

(iii) What is the least possible number of women who spent more than 50 minutes in the boutique?

(iv) The sentences below describe the type of data shown in the histogram above. Delete the incorrect word in each pair of brackets.
This is a set of [qualitative/quantitative] data.
The data are [discrete/continuous].

Solution

(i)

Time (minutes)	0–15	15–30	30–45	45–60	60–75
Number of women	3	8	12	7	4

(ii) $3 + 8 + 12 + 7 + 4 = 34$ women in the group

(iii) The seven women in the class interval 45–60 minutes could all have spent less than 50 minutes in the boutique.

∴ Least possible number of women who spent more than 50 minutes in the boutique is four, i.e. all those in the class interval 60–70 minutes.

(iv) This is a set of [~~qualitative~~/quantitative] data.

The data are [~~discrete~~/continuous].

key point

- Time is a quantity.
- Time is continuous, e.g 15 minutes and 43 seconds; 58·99 minutes; $20\frac{1}{9}$ minutes, etc.

exam focus

It is useful to remember that:
- Bar charts have equal gaps between the bars.
- Histograms have no gaps between the bars.
- Bar charts can only represent discrete data.
- Histograms can represent discrete or continuous data.

exam Q

Data on the type of broadband connection used by enterprises in Ireland for 2008 and 2009 are contained in the table below.

	2008	2009
	%	%
Broadband connection	84	84
By type of connection		
DSL (<2Mb/s)	31	29
DSL (>2Mb/s)	41	45
Other fixed connection	31	20
Mobile broadband	24	27

Source: Central Statistics Office

(a) Display the data in a way that allows you to compare the data for the two years.

(b) Identify any trends that you think are shown by the data.

Solution

(a)

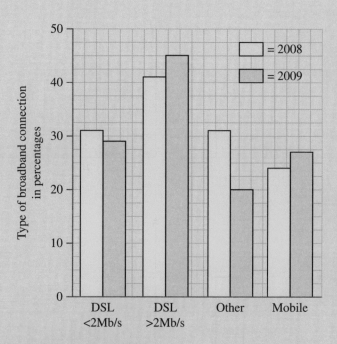

(b) • Overall there was no change in total broadband connection.
  • The percentage of slower (<2Mb/s) connections went down.
  • The percentage of faster (>2Mb/s) connections went up.
  • The percentage of other fixed connections went down a lot.
  • Mobile went up slightly in terms of percentage.

This list is not exhaustive. You may have others.

exam focus

  • Part (b) required 3 trends for full marks.
  • The total marks awarded for the question including (a) and (b) were 10.
  • A total of 8 out of 10 marks were awarded for the correct answer for part (a) or part (b). That is a high partial credit of 8 out of 10 marks for either part.

From this marking scheme you can understand how vital it is for you to attempt every question to the best of your ability.

Distributions and shapes of histograms

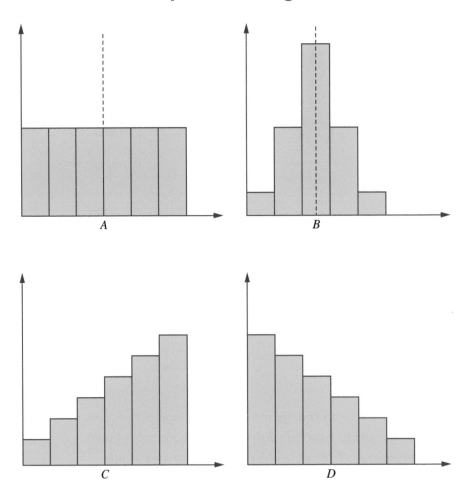

Histograms come in many different shapes. Above we have four histograms, all with different shapes:

- *A* has uniform distribution and is symmetric (balanced).
- *B* has a symmetric shape.
- *C* has no axis of symmetry. It is negatively skewed, that is, there is a tail at the negative end of the distribution.
- *D* has no axis of symmetry and is positively skewed.

A group of 80 students is randomly divided into two classes, each containing 40 students. Both classes take the same examination. The results are given below in a frequency table.

Marks	Class P Number of students	Class Q Number of students
0–10	0	3
10–20	13	20
20–30	22	7
30–40	4	6
40–50	1	4

(Note: 0–10 means 0 marks or more but less than 10 marks, etc.)

(i) Draw separate histograms for Class P and Class Q.

(ii) Compare the features of the two histograms. Use them to describe two similarities or differences between Class P and Class Q.

Students scoring 15 marks or less must take the class and the examination again.

(iii) Use your graphs, showing your method clearly, to estimate how many students, in total, must take the class and the examination again.

(iv) Would you advise these students to attempt to be in Class P or Class Q? Give a reason.

Solution

(i)

Class P

Marks	0–10	10–20	20–30	30–40	40–50
Number of students	0	13	22	4	1

Class Q

Marks	0–10	10–20	20–30	30–40	40–50
Number of students	3	20	7	6	4

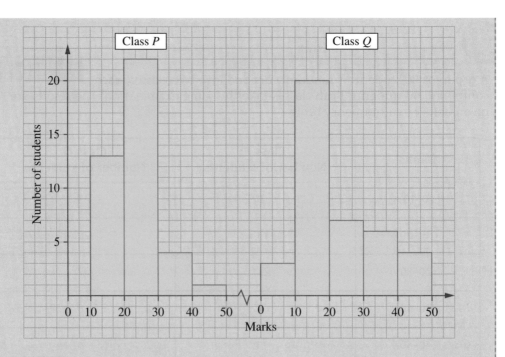

(ii) From the histograms, the marks for class Q are more spread out. Class P seems to have better results overall.

(iii)

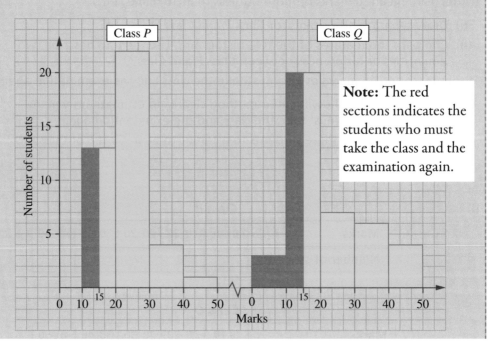

Note: The red sections indicates the students who must take the class and the examination again.

<15 marks in Class *P* corresponds to half the number of students in the 10–20 marks section.

$$= \frac{1}{2}(13) = 6\frac{1}{2}$$

i.e. 6 or 7 students

<15 marks in Class *Q* corresponds to all students in the 0–10 marks section plus half the number of students in the 10–20 marks section.

$$= 3 + \frac{1}{2}(20)$$
$$= 3 + 10$$
$$= 13 \text{ students}$$

(iv) Advise students to be in Class *P*, as fewer students from *P* have to take the examination again.

Stem and leaf diagrams

A stem and leaf diagram is a useful way of presenting data. It shows all the original data and gives the overall picture or shape of the distribution.

It is similar to a horizontal histogram, with the numbers forming the rectangles.
The given numbers on the stem and leaf plot can be more useful than a histogram in calculations.

Stem and leaf diagrams are suitable only for small amounts of data.

The ages of a group of 12 people are given as:

$$6, 8, 12, 15, 17, 23, 23, 28, 30, 32, 37, 44$$

This can be represented on an ordered stem and leaf diagram as shown below.

0	6	8	
1	2	5	7
2	3	3	⑧
3	0	2	7
4	4		

This represents 28:
stem = 2, leaf = 8.

Key: $1|7 = 17$

You must always add a key to show how the stem and leaf combine.

An educator believes that Project Maths methods will help Leaving Certificate students improve their maths grades. She arranges for a Leaving Certificate class of 21 students to take part in Project Maths methods for a one-year period.

A control class of 24 Leaving Certificate students follows the traditional maths methods. At the end of the year, a maths test is given to all students. The results in percentages are given on the ordered back-to-back stem and leaf plots.

4	3	1 9
5 4	4	2 2
8 7 6 2	5	1 3 7 9 9 9
8 6 6 3 3 1	6	0 6 2 8
7 6 3 2 2	7	1 1 3 5
8 5 4	8	1 2 8

Write down four errors in the above ordered back-to-back stem and leaf plot.

Solution

Error 1: The plot does not indicate which group is traditional and which is Project Maths.

Error 2: The right-hand side line is not ordered.

	6	0 6 2 8

It should read:

	6	0 2 6 8

Error 3: There are 21 readings on both sides of the plot. One side should have 24 readings.

Error 4: No key on either side.

     e.g.   Right-hand side $7|3 = 73\%$

            Left-hand side $6|5 = 56\%$

John's third-year Physical Education class did a fitness test. The number of sit-ups that each student did in one minute is recorded below:

| 59 | 48 | 27 | 53 | 36 | 29 | 52 | 46 | 45 | 37 | 49 | 51 |
| 33 | 45 | 38 | 52 | 40 | 51 | 37 | 44 | 47 | 45 | 60 | 41 |

The students practised this exercise for the next three weeks and then repeated the test in the same order. The data for the second test are as follows:

| 61 | 52 | 33 | 51 | 39 | 40 | 50 | 49 | 46 | 37 | 59 | 49 |
| 38 | 48 | 39 | 58 | 44 | 52 | 38 | 44 | 49 | 51 | 62 | 44 |

(a) Represent the data from the two tests on a back-to-back stem-and-leaf diagram.

	Test 2									Test 1	
						2					
						3					
						4					
						5					
						6					
						Key:					

(b) How many students are in the class?

(c) What is the *range* of sit-ups for the class?

(d) Based on the data and the diagram, do you think that practice improves the ability to do sit-ups? Give a reason for your answer.

(e) John did 41 sit-ups in Test 1 and 44 in Test 2. How did his performance compare with that of the rest of the class?

35 marks were awarded for this question with a suggested maximum time of 10 minutes. This gives a mark-to-time ratio of $35:10 = 3.5:1$, which is very high.

It is particularly important to do well here. The exam may not always be, consistent with the relationship between maximum time allocated and marks awarded.

Solution

(a) The question does not ask for, nor does it provide, the required space for an **ordered** back-to-back stem and leaf diagram.

It's good practise to ask the exam superintendent for extra paper and do your work there.

When constructing stem-and-leaf diagrams:

1. Construct an unordered diagram

2. From the unordered diagram, construct an ordered one (as shown below).

Unordered diagram:

		Test 2										Test 1								
										2	7	9								
			8	9	8	7	9	3	3	6	7	3	8	7						
4	9	4	4	8	9	6	9	0	4	8	6	5	9	5	0	4	7	5	1	
		1	2	8	9	0	1	2	5	9	3	2	1	2	1					
							2	1	6	0										

Key: 9|3 = 39 Sit-ups   Key: 3|6 = 36 Sit-ups

Ordered diagram:

		Test 2										Test 1								
										2	7	9								
			9	9	8	8	7	3	3	3	6	7	7	8						
9	9	9	8	6	4	4	4	0	4	0	1	4	5	5	5	6	7	8	9	
		9	8	2	2	1	1	0	5	1	1	2	2	3	9					
							2	1	6	0										

Key: 9|3 = 39 Sit-ups   Key: 3|6 = 36 Sit-ups

(b) 24 students in the class

(c) Range of sit-ups = Highest − Lowest

For Test 1, Range = 60 − 27 = 33

For Test 2, Range = 62 − 33 = 29

(d) By observing informally the results in the ordered stem-and-leaf diagram its difficult to see improvement.

Totalling both tests gives 1,065 sit-ups on Test 1 and 1,133 sit-ups on Test 2.

This might lead us to conclude that there is a slight improvement.

(e) Mean on Test 1 = $\dfrac{\text{Total sit-ups}}{\text{Total students}} = \dfrac{1{,}065}{24} = 44{\cdot}375$

Mean on Test 2 = $\dfrac{\text{Total sit-ups}}{\text{Total students}} = \dfrac{1{,}133}{24} = 47{\cdot}2$

Mean improvement per student = $47{\cdot}2 - 44{\cdot}375 = 2{\cdot}825$

John's improvement $(44 - 41)$ is 3 sit-ups.

As $3 > 2{\cdot}825$, we could say John compares favourably with the class.

However, it is difficult to draw a definite conclusion from the data.

From the ordered stem and leaf we can observe John finished:

— In 16th place in Test 1

— In 16th place (joint 15th with three students) in Test 2

This shows no improvement.

Part (a) in the above exam question was awarded a total of 15 marks. It is vital to keep your concentration, construct **two** diagrams and check your work by counting the data on the diagrams to ensure you have 24 data points.

Part (b) was awarded 5 marks.

Part (c) was awarded a total of 10 marks with 8 marks for **one** correct range.

Part (d) and (e) together were awarded a total of 5 marks. Write something down about John's performance.

The ages of the Academy Award winners for best male actor and best female actor (at the time they won the award) from 1992 to 2011 are as follows:

Male actor   54 52 37 38 32 45 60 46 40 36 47 29 43 37 38 45 50 48 60 50

Female actor 42 29 33 36 45 49 39 26 25 33 35 35 28 30 29 61 32 33 45 29

(a) Represent the data on a back-to-back stem and leaf diagram.

Male actors								Female actors				
						2						
						3						
						4						
						5						
						6						
Key:						Key:						

(b) State one similarity and one difference that can be observed between the ages of the male and female winners.

(c) Mary says, 'The female winners were younger than the male winners.' Investigate this statement in relation to:

   (i) The mean age of the male winners and mean age of the female winners

   (ii) The median age of the male winners and the median age of the female winners.

(d) Find the interquartile ranges of the ages of the male winners and of the female winners.

Solution

(a) The question is much easier to answer if we construct an **ordered** stem-and-leaf diagram.

27 marks awarded for this question with a suggested maximum time of 15 minutes. This gives a mark-to-time ratio of $27:15 = 1·8:10$, which is slightly lower than we might expect.

	Male actors									Female actors						
							9	2	9	6	5	8	9	9		
Unordered diagram		8	7	6	2	8	7	3	3	6	9	3	5	5	0	2	3
	8	5	3	7	0	6	5	4	2	5	9	5				
				0	0	2	4	5								
					0	0	6	1								
	Key: $2\|4 = 42$ years							**Key:** $3\|9 = 39$ years								

Ordered diagram

Male actors							Stem	Female actors								
						9	2	5	6	8	9	9	9			
8	8	7	7	6	2		3	0	2	3	3	3	5	5	6	9
8	7	6	5	5	3	0	4	2	5	5	9					
			4	2	0	0	5									
					0	0	6	1								

Key: $2|4 = 42$ years   Key: $3|9 = 39$ years

(b) One similarity from: No one aged over 61

No one aged under 24

Age range of males similar to age range of females

One difference from: One female outlier no male outlier

Females are younger, overall

No female in 50s

(c) (i) Total age of males = 887 $\Rightarrow$ Mean age males $= \dfrac{887}{20} = 44{\cdot}35$ years

Total age of females = 714 $\Rightarrow$ Mean age females $= \dfrac{714}{20} = 35{\cdot}7$ years

By comparison, we conclude females were younger

(ii) From the ordered stem and leaf diagram ↓ marks the position of the median:

Median age of male winners = Middle age from the diagram

$$= \frac{45 + 45}{2} = 45 \text{ years}$$

Median age of female winners = Middle age from the diagram

$$= \frac{33 + 33}{2} = 33 \text{ years}$$

By comparison, we conclude females were younger

(d) The interquartile range is given by $Q_3 - Q_1$ (see previous chapter)

We may read Q_3 and Q_1 from the ordered stem and leaf diagram for both males and females to find:

Male actors

$Q_1 = \dfrac{37 + 38}{2} = 37{\cdot}5$

$Q_3 = \dfrac{50 + 50}{2} = 50$

Interquartile range $= 50 - 37{\cdot}5$
$= 12{\cdot}5$ years

Female actors

$Q_1 = \dfrac{29 + 29}{2} = 29$

$Q_3 = \dfrac{39 + 42}{2} = 40{\cdot}5$

Interquartile range $= 40{\cdot}5 - 29$
$= 11{\cdot}5$ years

This question was worth a total of 27 marks

Part (a) was awarded 5 marks. Good concentration is required to get this straightforward question correct. Remember the ordered diagram was not required for full marks.

Part (b) was awarded 5 marks for a correct similarity and 5 marks for a correct difference.

Part (c) (i) and (ii) were awarded 5 marks each for the correct answer. It was well answered.

Part (d) was awarded 2 marks. This part was very badly answered by candidates. Do your best on each part. Write something for each part but do not get bogged down in a question. Watch your time budget.

Pie charts

A pie chart is a circle divided into sectors in proportion to the frequency of the data. It displays the proportions as angles, measured from the centre of the circle.

Steps in drawing a pie chart:

1. Add up all the frequencies.
2. Divide this total into 360°.
3. Multiply the answer in step 2 by each individual frequency. (This gives the size of the angle for each sector.)
4. Draw the pie chart, label each sector, and give it a title. (It is a good idea to write the size of each angle on the pie chart.)

key point

It is good practice to check that all your angles add up to 360° before drawing the pie chart.

Example

144 third-year pupils were asked to chose from an option of 4 activities. The results are in the table below

Watch TV	Play computer games	Go on Facebook	Take a walk
30	48	42	24

Illustrate the data with a pie chart.

Solution

144 pupils are to be represented by 360°.

Thus, 144 pupils = 360° (degrees on the right, because we want our answer in degrees)

∴ 1 pupil = 2·5° (divide both sides by 144)

In other words, one pupil will take up 2·5° on the pie chart.

Draw a table to work out the angle for each sector.

Sector	Number of pupils	Angle
Watch TV	30	30 × 2·5° = 75°
Play computer games	48	48 × 2·5° = 120°
Go on Facebook	42	42 × 2·5° = 105°
Take a walk	24	24 × 2·5° = 60°
Total	144	360°

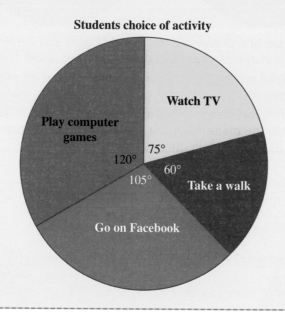

Students choice of activity

In total, 7,150 second level school students from 216 schools completed the 2011/2012 phase 11 *CensusAtSchool* questionnaire. The questionnaire contained a question relating to where students keep their mobile phones while sleeping.

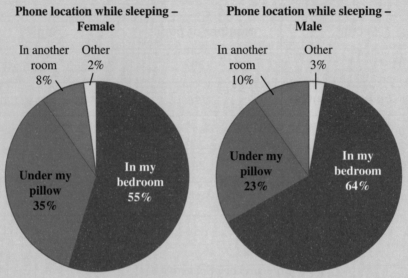

Phone location while sleeping – Female

In another room 8%
Other 2%

In my bedroom 55%

Under my pillow 35%

Phone location while sleeping – Male

In another room 10%
Other 3%

Under my pillow 23%

In my bedroom 64%

(a) Given that this question was answered by 4,171 girls and 2,979 boys, calculate how many female students kept their mobile phones under their pillows.

(b) Calculate the overall percentage of students who kept their mobile phones under their pillows.

(c) A new pie chart is to be drawn showing the mobile phone location for all students. Calculate the measure of the angle that would represent the students who kept their mobile phones under their pillows.

Solution

(a) The total number of female students = 100% = 4,171

$$\therefore 1\% = \frac{4,171}{100} = 41 \cdot 71$$

The number of female students with phone under pillow = 35% = 41·71 × 35
= 1,460 approx

(b) The total number of male students = 100% = 2,979

$$\therefore 1\% = \frac{2,979}{100} = 29 \cdot 79$$

The number of male students with phone under pillow = 23% = 29·79 × 23
= 685 approx

Hence, total number of students with phone under pillow = 1,460 + 685 = 2,145

Total number of students = 4,171 + 2,979 = 7,150

This means the overall percentage of students who kept their mobile phone under their pillows is given by

$$\frac{2,145}{7,150} \times 100 = 30\%$$

(c) The new pie chart would have an angle of 30% to represent the students who kept their mobile phones under their pillows:

$$\therefore \quad 100\% = 360°$$

$$1\% = \frac{360}{100} = 3.6°$$

$$30\% = 3.6° \times 30 = 108°$$

There are 24 students in a class. On a Friday, each student present in class is asked for the number of days they had been absent that week. The results are recorded in the table below.

Number of days absent	None	One	Two	Three	Four	Five
Number of students	9	2	3	4	1	0

(a) How many students were absent on that Friday?

(b) On the following Monday, all of the students were present in class and the table was updated to include the entire class. Which number from the above table could not have changed? Give a reason for your answer.

(c) The total number of days that were missed during the week will depend on the answers given by the students who were absent on Friday. Complete the tables below to show how the largest possible and smallest possible number of days missed would arise.

Smallest possible number of days missed					
Number of days absent	None	One	Two	Three	Four	Five
Number of students						

Largest possible number of days missed					
Number of days absent	None	One	Two	Three	Four	Five
Number of students						

(d) Cathal decides to draw a pie chart of the actual data collected on Monday. He calculates the number of degrees for each sector of the pie chart. Use this data to calculate the mean number of absences per pupil for the previous week, correct to one place of decimals.

Number of days absent	None	One	Two	Three	Four	Five
Number of students						
Number of degrees	135°	30°	75°	60°	45°	15°

Solution

(a) $24 - (9 + 2 + 3 + 4 + 1 + 0) = 24 - 19 = 5$

(b) The '9' students who missed no days would not change. Another way of saying this is 'None' would not change.

The reason is that the 5 students who were absent on the Friday would fall under one of the other five categories since they had missed at least one day (the Friday).

(c)

Smallest possible number of days missed						
Number of days absent	None	One	Two	Three	Four	Five
Number of students	9	7	3	4	1	0

Largest possible number of days missed						
Number of days absent	None	One	Two	Three	Four	Five
Number of students	9	2	3	4	1	5

(d) $\dfrac{135}{360} \times 24 = 9$ $\qquad \dfrac{60}{360} \times 24 = 4$

$\dfrac{30}{360} \times 24 = 2$ $\qquad \dfrac{45}{360} \times 24 = 3$

$\dfrac{75}{360} \times 24 = 5$ $\qquad \dfrac{15}{360} \times 24 = 1$

This gives us:

Number of days absent	None	One	Two	Three	Four	Five
Number of students	9	2	5	4	3	1
Number of degrees	135°	30°	75°	60°	45°	15°

$$\text{Mean} = \frac{(9)(0) + (2)(1) + (5)(2) + (4)(3) + (3)(4) + (1)(5)}{9 + 2 + 5 + 4 + 3 + 1}$$

$$= \frac{0 + 2 + 10 + 12 + 12 + 5}{24} = \frac{41}{24} = 1 \cdot 7$$

Example

From the methods of representing data that you have studied, state which method you would use to represent the following three data sets.

Hence, use your choice to represent each data set. You may use a different method for each case.

(i) The number of people in each car as it crossed a toll bridge was recorded as follows:

1	2	1	2	4	1	1	1	3	2	1	2	4
1	3	7	2	3	5	4	1	2	5	1	1	3
1	1	3	4	2	5	2	3	2	3	2	1	3

(ii) The grades awarded in a class of students were as follows:

B	A	C	D	C	C	C	B	D	C
A	D	C	B	B	C	B	C	B	D
C	B	B	C	A	C	B	C	B	C

(iii) The number of students studying in a certain university was as follows:

Year	First year	Second year	Third year	Fourth year
Number of students	690	540	480	470

Solution

(i) A line plot would be an excellent way to represent this data because it gives a very clear picture and it could be carried out as the cars passed the toll bridge.

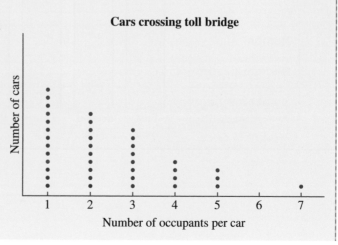

Cars crossing toll bridge

(ii) 3 Grade A; 10 Grade B; 13 Grade C; 4 Grade D.

30 students with only four different grades would be clearly represented on a pie chart.

30 students = 360°

$$1 \text{ student } = \frac{360}{30} = 12°$$

3 grade A students = 12 × 3 = 36°

10 grade B students = 12 × 10 = 120°

13 grade C students = 12 × 13 = 156°

4 grade D students = 12 × 4 = 48°

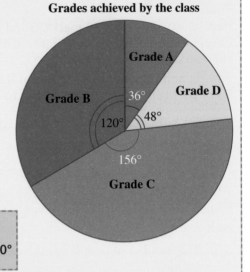

Grades achieved by the class

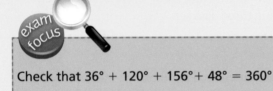

Check that 36° + 120° + 156° + 48° = 360°

(iii) A bar chart (or histogram) is a very clear way to show this information:

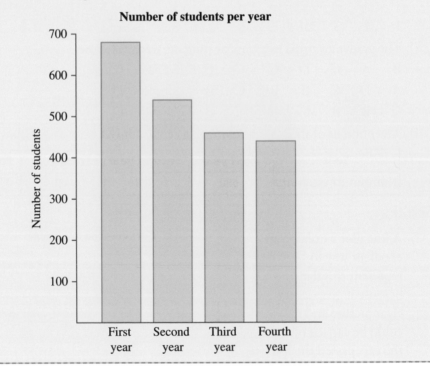

Number of students per year

Misuses of statistics
Misleading graphs and diagrams

Many advertisements frequently use graphs and diagrams to present information. In most cases, the graphs and diagrams are well presented and give an honest and fair representation of the facts. However, some are deliberately drawn to mislead. The most common methods to present correct information in misleading graphs and diagrams is to:

- use a false origin
- insert no scale or a non-uniform scale on the vertical axis
- draw graphs with unequal widths and dimensions.

Other misleading methods to watch out for are using a biased sample or a sample that is too small; deliberate omissions, errors and exaggerations; misleading comparisons; and using unreliable sources.

Consumers should try to spot misleading graphs and diagrams, errors, omissions and exaggerations when presented with information (statistics).

Example

The pie chart displays data on the percentages of Leaving Certificate students taking mathematics at different levels in an exam.
Find two aspects of the pie chart which are incorrect.

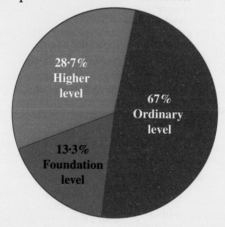

Solution

28·7% + 13·3% + 67% = 109% which is incorrect, it should total 100% and 67% at Ordinary Level should occupy more than half the pie chart.

Glossary of Statistical Terms

This glossary is to help your understanding of statistical terms. You are not required to learn these terms off by heart.

Arithmetic mean   A measure of central tendency that sums all the scores in the data sets and divides by the number of scores.

Bias   Systematic errors in the way the sample represents the population. It can be caused by poorly worded surveys, non response or undercoverage.

Categorical data   Non-numerical data that can be counted but only described in words. Such data may be ordered or unordered.

Class interval   The upper and lower boundary of a set of scores used in the creation of a frequency distribution.

Continuous numerical data   Data which can take any numerical value within a certain range.

Cumulative frequency distribution   A frequency distribution that shows frequencies for class intervals along with the cumulative frequency for each.

Data   Any collection of variables.

Data point   An observation.

Data set   A set of data points.

Dependent variable   Often denoted by y, whose value depends on another variable. It is usually represented on the vertical axis.

Descriptive statistics   Values that describe the characteristics of a sample or population.

Discrete numerical data   Data which can only have certain values.

Frequency distribution   A method for illustrating the distribution of scores within class intervals. Often given in tabular form (frequency distribution table).

Frequency polygon   A graphical representation of a frequency distribution.

Histogram   A graphical representation of a frequency distribution.

Independent variable   Often denoted by x, whose variation does not depend on another variable. It is usually represented on the horizontal axis.

Inferential statistics   Tools that are used to infer the results based on a sample to a population.

Mean   The value where scores are summed and divided by the number of observations.

Measures of central tendency   The mean, median and mode.

Median   The point at which 50% of the cases in a distribution fall below and 50% fall above.

Mid-interval value   The central value in a class interval.

Mode   The most frequently occurring score in a distribution.

Nominal data   Categorical data that has no order.

Numerical data   Data that can be counted or measured.

Observed score   The score that is recorded or observed.

Obtained value   The value that results from the application of a statistical test.

Ordinal data   Categorical data that has order.

Outlier   A point in a sample widely separated from the main cluster of points in the sample.

Population   The complete set of data under consideration.

Primary data   First-hand data that you collect yourself or are collected by someone under your direct supervision.

Qualitative data   A type of information that describes or characterises, but does not measure, data. Often referred to as categorical data.

Quantitative data   A type of information that can be counted or expressed numerically. Often referred to as numerical data.

Questionnaire   A set of questions used to obtain data from a population.

Random   Chosen without regard to any characteristics of the individual members of the population so that each has an equal chance of being selected.

Random sample   A sample selected so that its distribution can be taken to be representative of the whole population.

Range The highest value minus the lowest value.

Sample A subset of a population.

Secondary data Second-hand data that have already been collected and made available from an external source such as newspapers, government departments or the internet.

Skew or skewness The quality of a distribution that defines the disproportionate frequency of certain scores. A longer right tail than left corresponds to a smaller number of occurrences at the high end of the distribution: this is a *positively* skewed distribution. A shorter right tail than left corresponds to a larger number of occurrences at the high end of the distribution; this is a *negatively* skewed distribution.

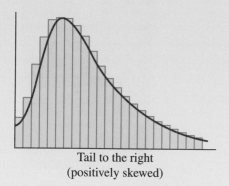

Tail to the right
(positively skewed)

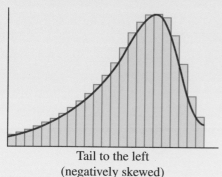

Tail to the left
(negatively skewed)

Spread How data are distributed.

Statistics A set of tools and techniques used to collect, organise, represent and interpret information.

Symmetric (normal) curve This distribution has an axis of symmetry down the middle. It is called a symmetrical distribution.

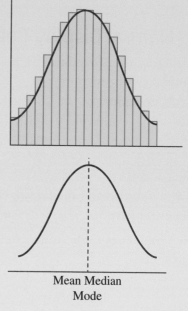

Mean Median
Mode

Unimodal A unimodal data set (distribution) has one peak of data.

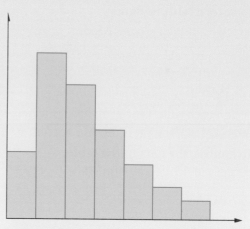

Univariate data A survey that looks at only one variable (data set). The variable may be either qualitative or quantitative. e.g. ages of the 7 dwarfs.

Variability The amount of spread or dispersion in a set of scores.

Calculator Instructions

Casio Natural Display Calculator

Before starting any procedures on the calculator, you should clear the memory:

To clear the memory:

> Shift *then* 9 : CLR
>
> 3 : All
>
> = : Yes
>
> [AC]

To perform a statistical calculation, you must create a frequency table.

To enter a frequency table, you must switch Frequency on:

> Shift *then* Mode
>
> Down Arrow
>
> 3 : STAT
>
> 1 : ON

To enter a table of data:

> Mode
>
> 2 : STAT
>
> 1 : 1-VAR

Enter the data into the table, followed by the = sign each time. Once you have finished entering the data, press the AC button.

To analyse the data in the table:

> Shift *then* 1 : STAT
>
> 4 : Var

Options are as follows:

$2 : \bar{x}$ (the mean of the terms, also known as μ)

For simplicity, to find the mean of a **single list of data,** create a frequency table and set all the frequencies to 1.

Practice exercise

Use your calculator to find the mean of the following table of data:

Value	2	4	6	8	10
Frequency	13	6	9	2	6

The answer is: Mean $\mu = \bar{x} = 5$

Sharp WriteView Calculator

Before starting any procedures on the calculator, you should clear the memory:

To clear the memory:

> 2nd F *then* ALPHA : M-CLR
>> 1 : Memory
>> 0 : Clear

To put the calculator into Statistics mode:

> Mode
>> 1 : STAT

To enter the data:

> Take each value and frequency as a pair of data.
>> Enter each pair, separated by a comma.
>>> Then press the DATA button
>>> (e.g. enter: 2, 13 DATA).

Once all the pairs of data have been entered, press:

> ON / C

key point

To find the mean of a **single list of data,** press the DATA button after each value. Leave out the comma and frequency value.

To analyse the data entered:

ALPHA *then* 4 *then* $= : \bar{x}$ (the mean of the terms, also known as μ)

Practice exercise

Use your calculator to find the mean of the following table of data:

Value	2	4	6	8	10
Frequency	13	6	9	2	6

The answer is: Mean $\mu = \bar{x} = 5$